THE SPANISH LADIE
and two other stories from
CERVANTES

THE SPANISH LADIE

AND TWO OTHER STORIES FROM
CERVANTES TRANSLATED FROM
THE ORIGINAL BY JAMES MABBE
1640

AND NEWLY ILLUSTRATED BY
DOUGLAS PERCY BLISS

OXFORD UNIVERSITY PRESS
LONDON: HUMPHREY MILFORD
1928

Printed in Great Britain at the University Press, Oxford

Illustrations stencilled in colour at the Curwen Press

CONTENTS

THE SPANISH LADIE

Mongst those many spoyles which the Conquerours of the famous Northern Island (governed then by a most noble Queene) carried away from the Citie of *Cadiz*; *Clotaldo*, Captaine of a squadron of Ships, brought along with him to *Mundolin,* metropolis of that Isle, a Girle of the age of seven yeares, little more or lesse, and this contrary to the will and knowledge of the Generall; who with great diligence caused search to bee made for the Childe, that she might bee returned backe to her Parents, who had complained unto him, of the wanting of their Daughter; humbly beseeching him, that since his Excellencie was pleased to content himselfe with their goods, and out of his noblenesse had left their persons free; that they onely might not be so miserable and unhappie, that seeing they were now left poore, they might not be robb'd of their Daughter, who was the joy of their hearts, the light of their eyes, and the fayrest and beautifullest creature that was in all the Citie. The Generall caused Proclamation to bee made throughout all the whole Fleet, that upon paine of death, he whosoever had the Childe, should restore her backe to her Parents. But no penalties, nor feares of punishment could move *Clotaldo* to obey the Generalls command. For he kept her very secret and close in his owne Ship, standing wonderfully affectioned, though very Christianly, to the incomparable beauty of *Isabella*, for so was the Childe called.

In conclusion, her Parents remained without her very sad and disconsolate, and *Clotaldo* beyond measure exceeding glad and joyfull. He arrived at *Mundolin,* and delivered up this fayre Mayde as a most rich spoyle, to his Wife. But as good lucke would have it, all they of *Clotaldo's* house were Christians in heart, though in publicke they made show to follow the religion of the Countrey.

B

Clotaldo had a Sonne named *Ricaredo,* about some 12. yeares of age, taught by his Parents to love and feare God. *Catalina* the Wife of *Clotaldo,* a noble Christian, and prudent Ladie, bare such great love and affection to *Isabella,* (that as if shee had beene her owne Daughter,) shee bred, cherished, industriated, and instructed her; and the Childe had such good naturall abilities, that shee did easily apprehend and learne whatsoever they taught her. With time, and the kinde usage shee received, she went forgetting those cockerings of her true Parents; but not so much that she did cease to thinke on them, and to sigh often for them. And although she went learning the tongue of the Island, yet did shee not lose her Spanish. For *Clotaldo* tooke care to bring *Spanyards* secretly to his house, to talke and converse with her. And

2

so without forgetting her owne naturall language, she spake the other as well as if she had been born in *Mundolin*.

After that they had taught her all manner of workes, which a well bred Damosell could, or ought to learne, they taught her to read and to write more then indifferently well. But that wherein shee did excell, was in playing upon all those Instruments of Musicke, which might with most decencie become a woman; accompanying the same with such a voyce which Heaven had bestowed on her in so rare and singular a kinde, that when she chaunted, she inchaunted all that heard her.

All these her acquired graces, besides those that were naturall unto her, went by little and little, kindling the coals of love in *Ricaredo's* heart; to whom as to her Masters Son, she wished all good and happinesse, and carried her selfe towards him with all faire respects.

At first love led him on with onely a kinde of liking and complacencie, in beholding the unmatchable beauty of *Isabella*; and in considering her infinite vertues and graces, and loving her as if shee had beene his Sister, his desires not going beyond their honest and vertuous bounds. But when as *Isabella* began to grow towards woman, (for then when *Ricaredo* burned in the flames of love shee was twelve yeares of age) that his former good will, and that complacencie and liking, was turned into most fervent desires of enjoying and possessing her, not that hee did aspire thereunto by any other meanes, then by those of being her Husband; since that from the incomparable beautie of *Isabel* (for so did they call her) no other thing could be hoped for, neither would hee himselfe, though hee could have expected that favour from her; because his noble condition, and the high esteeme wherein hee held *Isabella*, would not give the least way or consent, that any the least evill thought should take any rooting in his soule.

A thousand times did hee determine with himselfe to manifest the love he bare her to his Parents; and againe as oft did he not approve this his determination, because he knew that they had dedicated him for to bee the husband of a very rich and principall Gentlewoman, a Northern Damosell, who was likewise (like them) a close and concealed Christian. And it was cleare and apparant, (as he conceived, and said with himselfe) that they would not bee willing to give unto a slave (if this name may bee given to *Isabella*) that which they had treated, and in a manner concluded on to give to a gentlewoman. And therefore being much perplexed and pensive, not knowing what course to take for to attaine to the end of his good desire; he passed over such a kinde of life as had almost brought him to the point of losing it. But it seeming unto him to bee great cowardize and faintheartednesse, to suffer himselfe to dye without seeking out some kinde of remedie for his griefe; he did hearten and incourage himselfe to open his minde, and declare his intent to *Isabella*.

All they of the house were very sad and heavie, and much troubled by reason of *Ricaredo* his sicknesse (for hee was well beloved of them all,) but his Father and Mother exceeding sorrowfull, as well for that they had no other Childe, as also for that his great vertue, valour, and understanding did deserve it. The Phisitians did not hit right upon his disease, neither durst he, neither would he discover it unto them. In the end, being fully resolved to breake through these difficulties which hee imagined with himselfe; one day amongst the rest, that *Isabella* came in to serve and attend him, seeing her all alone, with a low voyce, and a troubled tongue, he spake unto her after this manner.

Faire *Isabella,* thy much worth, thy great vertue, and exceeding beautie, not to be equalled by any; have brought me to that extreamitie wherein you see me; and therefore if you will that I should leave my life in the hands of the greatest extreamitie that may bee imagined; let thy good desire be answerable unto mine, which is no other then to receive thee for my Spouse. But this must bee carried closely, and kept hid from my Parents, of whom I am afraid (who because they know that which I know, thy great deservingnesse) that they will denie mee that good which doth so much concerne mee. If thou wilt give me thy word to bee mine, I shall forthwith passe mine, as a true Christian to be thine. And put case that I should never come to enjoy thee, as I will not till that I have the Churches benediction, and my Parents good will, yet with this my imagining, that thou wilt be assuredly mine, it will be sufficient to recover me my health, and to make me live merrily and contented, till that happie and desired time shall come.

Whilest that *Ricaredo* discoursed thus with her, *Isabella* stood hearkening unto him with downe cast eyes, shewing in that her modest and sober looke, that her honestie did equall her beautie, and her circumspection, her great discretion. And seeing that *Ricaredo* had made an end of speaking, and was silent; this honest, faire, and discreet Damosell made him this answer.

Since that the rigour or clemency of Heaven (for I know not to which of these extreames I may attribute it) would (*Signior Ricaredo*) quit me of my Parents, and give me unto yours, (thankefully acknowledging the infinite favours they have done me.) I resolved with my selfe, that my will should never be any other then theirs; and therefore without it, the inestimable grace and favour which you are willing to doe mee, I should not hold it a happinesse, but a miserie, not a good, but a bad fortune. But if they being made acquainted therewith, I might bee so happie as to deserve you, from this day forward I offer unto you that will and consent which they shall give mee. And in the meane while that this shall be or deferred, or not at all effected; let your desires entertaine themselves with this, that mine shall bee eternall, and pure, in wishing you all that good which Heaven can give you.

Here did *Isabella* put a period to her honest and discreet words, and there began *Ricaredo's* recoverie. And now began to bee revived those hopes of his Parents, which in this his sicknesse were almost quite dead.

These two modest Lovers with a great deale of courtesie and kindnesse tooke leave each of other; he with tears in his eyes, shee with admiration in her soule, to see that *Ricaredo* should render up his love, to hers. Who being raysed from his bed (to his Parents seeming) by miracle; hee would not now any longer conceale his thoughts, and therefore one day he manifested them to his Mother, telling her in the end of his discourse, that if they did not Marrie him to *Isabella,* that to denie him her, and give him his death, it was one and the same thing. With such words, and with such endearings *Ricaredo* did extoll to the Heavens the vertues of *Isabella,* that it seemed to his Mother, that *Isabella* had not wrought upon her Son to win him to be her Husband. She did put her Son in good hope so to dispose his Father, that he might like as well thereof, as she did. And it so fell out, that repeating to her Husband word by word, what her Son had sayd unto her, he was easily moved to give way to that which his Son so earnestly desired, framing excuses to hinder that Marriage, which was in a manner agreed upon for the Northern Damosell.

When this was in agitation, *Isabella* was 14. yeares of age, and *Ricaredo* 20. And in these their so green and flourishing years, their great dis-cretion and knowne prudence, made them ancient.

There were but foure dayes wanting to come, which being accom-plished, *Ricaredo* his Parents were willing that their Sonne should enter into the state of Matrimonie, holding themselves both wise, and happie, in having chosen their prisoner to be their Daughter, esteem-ing more the dowrie of her vertues, then the great store of wealth that was offered with the Northerne Damosell.

The wedding clothes were already made, their kinsfolk and friends invited thereunto; and there was no other thing wanting, save making the Queene acquainted with the Marriage, because without her good will and consent, amongst those of noble bloud, not any Marriage is effected; but they doubted not of her good leave, and licence, and therefore had so long deferred the craving of it.

I say then, that all things standing in this estate, when there wanted but foure dayes till that of the wedding, one evening gave disturbance to all this their joy. A servant of the Queenes came and brought a message to *Clotaldo,* with expresse command from her Majestie, that the next morning he should bring to her Presence his Spanish Prisoner that he brought from *Cadiz. Clotaldo* returned answer, that her Majesties pleasure should most willingly bee obeyed. The Gentle-man having delivered his message, and received his answer, went his way, leaving the hearts of all the whole house full of passion, perturba-tions, and feares.

Aye me (sayd the Ladie *Catalina*) if it bee come to the Queenes knowledge that I have bred up this Childe in the Christian religion; and shall from thence inferre that all we of this Familie are Christians. Besides, if the Queene shall aske her what she hath learned in eight yeares since that she was our prisoner; what can the poore harmlesse soule answer, which shall not (notwithstanding all her discretion) condemne us?

Which *Isabella* hearing, spake thus unto her.

Let not (deare Ladie) this feare give you any trouble at all; for my trust is in God that he will put words into my mouth at that instant, out of his Divine Mercie towards me; that shall not onely not con-demne you, but that shall much redound to your good.

Ricaredo was much startled therewith, as divining therby some ill successe. *Clotaldo* sought out meanes that might give some courage to his great feare, but found none, save in the great confidence which he had in God, and in the wisedome of *Isabella*; who earnestly entreated her, that by all the wayes she possibly could devise, she should excuse her condemning of them to be Christians; for though in spirit they were readie to receive Martyrdome; yet notwithstanding, the flesh was weake, and were loth to drinke of that bitter cup.

Not once, but often *Isabella* assured them to rest assured, that for her

7

cause, or any default of hers, that should not succeed which they feared and suspected. For albeit she then knew not what answer to make to those Interrogatories and questions, which in such a case as this might be put unto her; yet had she such a lively and assured hope that she should answer thereunto in such sort (as she had at other times told them) that her answers should rather doe them good then hurt.

They discoursed that night on many things, especially on this particular; that if the Queene had knowne that they were Christians, shee would not have sent them so milde a message; whence they might inferre, that shee was onely desirous to see *Isabella,* whose unequalled beautie and abilitie had come to her eares, and to those of the Court, as it did to all those of the Citie. But because they had not before this presented her unto her Majestie, they found themselves faulty; of which fault, they thought good to excuse themselves, by saying; that from that very instant that she came into his power, he had made choice of her, and as it were marked her out for to be the wife of his Sonne *Ricaredo.* But in this too, they likewise found themselves faultie, for having made such a match without her Majesties leave, and licence; howbeit this fault did not seeme unto them worthy of any great punishment. With this they comforted themselves, and agreed amongst themselves by a joynt consent, that *Isabella* should not goe meanely clad to Court, but like a Bride, since that shee was the Spouse of his Sonne *Ricaredo.*

Being thus resolved, the next day they apparrelled *Isabella* after the Spanish fashion; in a gowne of green Sattin cut upon cloth of gold, embroydered with Esses of pearles, wearing a great chaine of most rich orient pearles about her necke, having a hatband of Diamonds, and a Fanne in her hand, after the manner of your Spanish Ladies. Her haires of her head, which were full and long, and of a bright pleasing colour, sowen, and interwoven with Diamonds, and Pearles, did serve her instead of a coyfe. With this most rich dressing and lively disposition, and admirable beautie, She shewed her selfe that day in *Mundolin,* riding in a faire Caroch, carrying along with her, taken by so beautifull a sight, the soules and eyes of as many as looked on her. There were with her in the same Caroch, *Clotaldo* and his wife, and *Ricaredo,* and on horse back many noble gentlemen of their

kindred, and Alliance. All this honour *Clotaldo* was willing to do his Prisoner, for to obliege the Queene to use her as the Spouse of his Son.

Being come now to the Court, and brought into the Chamber of Presence where the Queene was, *Isabella* entered thereinto; presenting there the fayrest show which can fall within the compasse of imagination. The roome was large and spacious, and the traine that came with her had not gone above two steps forward, but they stood stil; and *Isabella* alone by her selfe, advanced her selfe towards the State where the Queene sate; and being thus alone, she seemed to appeare just like that starre, or exhalation, which by the region of fire is wont to move it selfe in a cleare and quiet night; or like unto a ray, or beame of the Sunne; which at the opening of the day discovers it selfe betweene two mountaines. All this did she seeme to bee, or rather like a Commet which did prognosticate the inflaming and setting on fire many of those soules that were present, which love had throughly heated, if not burned with the rayes of those resplendant sunnes of beautifull *Isabella,* who full of humilitie, and courtesie, made her approaches by degrees, addressing her self to kneele down before the Queene, and then after a short pausing said thus unto her. May it please your most excellent Majestie, so far forth to honour this your servant, that she may kisse your royall hand; so shall I ever hereafter hold my selfe to be a Ladie, since that I have beene so happie, as to come to see your greatnesse.

The Queene continued looking upon her a good while, without speaking one word; it seeming unto her (as she afterwards told a great Ladie of her Bed-chamber) that shee had a starrified heaven before her; whose starres were those many Pearles, and Diamonds which *Isabella* bare about her. Her fayre face, and eyes were the Sunne and Moone; and take all together in the whole peece, shee was a new wonder of beautie. The Ladies that attended about the Queens Person, wished that they had beene all eyes, that there might not remaine any thing in, or about *Isabella,* which they might not behold and view at full. Some commended the quicknesse of her eyes, some the colour of her face, and purenesse of complexion; some the propernesse of her body, and some the sweetnes of her speech. And some likewise, who out of meere envie, said; the *Spaniard* is a very handsome gentlewoman, but her habite and dressing seemeth very strange, and out of fashion. After some little suspension, the Queene causing *Isabella* to rise up, she said unto her; speake (pretty Mayd) unto mee in Spanish, for I understand it well, and shall take much pleasure therein. And turning her selfe towards *Clotaldo,* she sayd unto him.

Clotaldo, you have done Vs wrong, in keeping this treasure so long concealed from Vs; but it is such, and so rich, that it hath moved you to covetousnesse; you are bound to restore it unto Vs, for by right it is Ours, and properly belongeth unto Vs.

Madam (answered *Clotaldo*) it is true which your Majestie sayth; I confesse my fault, if it bee a fault to have kept this treasure, that it might be preserved in that perfection, as was fitting to appeare in your Majesties Presence. And now that it is here before your eye, I thought to have much improved it, by craving your Majesties leave that *Isabella* might be the Spouse of my Sonne *Ricaredo,* and to give your most excellent Majestie in these two, all that I am able to give you.

Her very name gives Vs very good content (replied the Queene) there could nothing have beene more wanting save the name of *Isabella* the *Spanyard,* to take off something from that perfection which is in her. But how is it (*Clotaldo*) that without Our leave you have promised her to your Sonne?

It is true Madam (answered *Clotaldo*) I have made him a promise of her, but it was upon the confidence that the many and notable services which my selfe, and my Auncestours have done this Crowne, might obtaine of your Majestie other more difficult favours, then this of your leave; and the rather, for that my Sonne is not yet espoused unto her.

Neither shall he (sayd the Queene) Marry *Isabella,* till he by himselfe, and in his owne person shall deserve her. Our meaning is, that I will not that either your owne or your Auncestors services, shall any whit benefit him in this particular; but that hee in his owne person shall dispose himselfe to serve mee, and for to merit for himselfe, and by his owne prowesse, this sweet pledge, whom we esteeme and reckon of as if she were our owne Daughter.

Isabella had scarce heard this last word delivered, when humbling her selfe againe on her knees before the Queene, she spake unto her in the Spanish tongue, to this effect.

As graces, which brings such graces with them (moſt noble Queene) are rather to be accounted happinesse, then misfortunes. And since that your Majeſtie hath beene pleased to grace me with the name of Daughter upon so good a pledge; what ill can I feare? or what good may I not hope for?

Looke what *Isabella* uttered, came from her so gracefully, and so wittingly, that the Queen ſtood extreamly affected towards her; and commanded that shee should remaine at Court in her service; and recommended her to a great Ladie, the chiefeſt amongſt those of her Bed-chamber, that shee might trayne her up according to the Court fashion.

Ricaredo, who saw that his life was taken away, in taking away *Isabella,* was readie almoſt to have loſt his wits; and therefore though overtaken with a tumbling and sudden passion of heart, he went and fell upon his knees before the Queen, and sayd unto her.

That I may serve your Majeſtie, I need not to be incited thereunto by any other rewards, then by those which my fore-fathers, and Aunceſtours have gotten by serving their Kings. But since that it is your Maieſties pleasure that I should serve you with good desires, and pretensions; I would gladly know, in what kinde, and in what employment I may manifeſt that I cumply; with that obligation which I owe unto your Maieſtie, and put my selfe to that which you shall impose upon me.

I have two Ships royall (answered the Queene) ready to put forth to Sea, whereof I have made Generall the *Baron* of *Lansac,* of one of these I make you Captaine, him Admirall, and you Vice-Admirall. For the bloud from whence you come, and runneth in your veines, doth assure mee that you will supply the defect of your yeares; and consider well the favour which wee doe you, since that therein I give you occasion, that corresponding with that which you are, and doing things answerable to the race from whence you come; by serving your

Queene, you may show the worth of your noble disposition, and of your person; and you shall receive thereby the greatest reward, which in your opinion you can wish or desire. I my selfe will be *Isabella's* Guard, though she give Vs manifest tokens, that her owne honestie will be her safest and surest guard. God blesse you in your Voyage; and since that you goe hence deepely (as I imagine) in love, I promise great matters unto my selfe of your noble exploits. Happy shall that King that goes to warre bee, who shall have in his Armie ten thousand Souldiers that are in love, for they will live in hope that the reward of their victories, shall be the enioying of their best beloved. Rise up *Ricaredo*, and bethinke your selfe if you will or have any thing to say to *Isabella*, for to morrow you must be gon.

Ricaredo kissed the Queenes hand, humbly thanking her, and highly esteeming the favour which she did him, and presently went from her to *Isabella*, and would feigne have spoken unto her, but could not, for love and grief had knit such a knot in his throat, and so tied his tongue, that had his life layen upon it, hee could not utter one word. But the water stood in his eies, and were so brimme-full, that they ranne over, and silently trickled downe his cheekes which he thought to dissemble and smother them, all that hee possibly could; yet not-withstanding could hee not hide them from the eyes of the Queene, and therefore she said unto him.

Thinke it no shame *Ricaredo* to weepe, neither valew your selfe the lesse, for having given at this your farewell such tender demonstrations of your heart. For it is one thing to fight with your enemies, and another thing to take your leave of her you love. *Isabella*, embrace *Ricaredo*, and give him your benediction, for his excessive sorrow, and loathnesse to leave you, doth very well deserve it.

Isabella, who stood amazed and astonished to see *Ricaredo's* tender heartednesse, and how truely he did grieve, and all for her sake, whom she loved as her Husband; did not understand what the Queene had commanded her, but began to shed teares; so without thinking what she did, and stood so still, and without any motion, that it seemed not to be a living soule, but a *Statua* of *Alablaster* that wept.

The affections of these two true and tender lovers, made the standers by to melt likewise into teares. And so *Ricaredo* without speaking a word to *Isabella,* or *Isabella* to him, they turned each from other, and *Clotaldo,* and they that came with him, doing reverence to the Queene, went out of the Presence full of compassion, discontent, and teares.

Isabella now remained like a poore Orphane, comming from the buriall of her Father and Mother, and as full now of feare, as before of griefe; least that her new Ladie to whom shee was recommended, would make her to change those manners and customes wherein she had been formerly bred up.

In conclusion, there shee remained, and within two daies after *Ricaredo* hoysed sayle, and put forth to Sea, beaten amongst many other with this thought, that he must do some notable peece of service, that might intitle him *the deserver of Isabella.*

But in conclusion, he besought Heaven to be propitious unto him, that such occasions might be offered unto him; wherein by shewing himselfe valiant, hee might cumply with the dutie of a Christian, leaving the Queene satisfied, and *Isabella* deserved.

Sixe daies these two Shippes sailed with a prosperous winde, shaping their course for the *Tercera* Islands; a place where never are wanting, either Ships of *Portugal,* from the *East-Indies,* or some that come thither from the *West-Indies.* And at sixe daies end there arose such a crosse-winde full in the teeth of them; and continued so long and so strong, that without suffering them to reach the Islands, they were inforced to make for *Spaine*; neere unto whose Coast, at the mouth of the Streight of *Gibraltar,* they descried three Ships; the one a very tall and goodly Ship, and the other two much lesse.

15

Ricaredo's Ship made up to that which was Admirall, for to know of his Generall, whether or no he would set upon those three Ships which they had descried. But before that he came up unto them; he might discerne that upon the toppe of the maine mast, there was hung out a blacke streamer, and comming a little neerer, he might hear Fifes, and Trumpets sounding faintly, and hoarsely; cleare and apparant signes that the Generall was dead, or some other principall person of the Shippe. At last comming within hearing, that they might speake one to another, which they had not done since their first putting forth; they might heare them from out the Admirall call out aloud unto them, to have the Vice-Admirall *Ricaredo* to come aboord their Ship, because the Generall the night before died of an Appoplexie.

All upon this newes were very sad, save *Ricaredo,* who was inwardly glad, not for the losse of his Generall, but to see that hee was left at libertie, and might freely command both Shippes; for so was it ordered by the Queene, that the Generall miscarrying, *Ricaredo* should succeed in his roome. Who presently went aboord the Admirall, where he found some that mourn'd for their dead General, and others that rejoyced with him that was now living. In a word, both the one and the other presently yeelded him obedience, and with short cere-monies cry'd him up for their Generall; two of those three Shippes which they had discovered not giving leave for greater, which going aloofe from the great Shippe, made up to the two Ships. They streight knew them to be Gallies, and Turkish Gallies, by the halfe Moones which they bare in their flagges, which gave *Ricaredo* great contentment; it seeming unto him, that that prize if Heaven should grant it him, would be of great benefit.

The Turkish Gallies came to know the Northern ships, who did not carry the Armes of the Island in their flagges, but of *Spaine,* for to deceive those that should chance to descrie them, and might take them to be Shippes of Piracie. The *Turkes* thought they had beene Shippes that had come from the *Indies,* wasted and spent with their long voyage, and that they would quickly yeeld and be taken. Wherupon, they came incroaching by little and little upon them, thinking presently to boord them, and *Ricaredo* suffered them to come neerer and neerer unto him, till he had them in command of his Ordnance, and then let flie at them, and giving them a broad side, discharged so luckily, and with such furie, that he shot one of the Gallies thorow, and thorow; so that one halfe of it lay all open, and naked, which forced them to flie, and make the best shift they could for to escape boording. The other Gallie seeing it's fellowes ill successe, made away in all haste, and strove to put her selfe under the side of the great Ship. But *Ricaredo,* who had Shippes that were light laden, and were quicke and nimble; and such excellent saylers, that they would turne and winde, and come off and on, as if they had beene plied with Oares; commanded them to charge the Ordnance anew, chasing them even to the ship, showring upon them a world of shot. They of the opened Gallie, as soone as they came to the ship, forsooke their Galley, and with all possible haste endeavoured to get into the ship. Which being per-ceived by *Ricaredo,* and that the sound Gallie imployed it selfe in relieving the other; he sets upon her with both his ships, and without giving her leave to tacke about, or to make any use of her Oares, he did put her to that streight and exigent, that the *Turkes* likewise that were in her, were forced to flee for refuge to the ship, not with any hope to defend themselves therein, or to stand it out in fight, but for to escape for the present with their lives. The *Christians* wherwith those Gallies were man'd, tearing up their bankes, and breaking their chaines, intermingled with the *Turkes,* sought to recover their ship; and as they were clambring up by the side of her, with musket shot from the ships, they went shooting at them, as at a marke; but *Ricaredo* gave order that they should shoot onely at the *Turkes,* and spare the

Christians. Thus were all the *Turkes* almost slaine; and they who entered the shippe with the Christians, for they were mingled one amongst another, making use of their weapons, were cut in peeces. For the force of the valiant when they begin to fall, must yeeld to the weakenesse of those that are rising. And therefore the Christians takeing heart, layed about them with such courage and mettle, that they did wonders for the working of their libertie; thinking all this while that those Northerne ships were *Spanish*.

In conclusion, the Christians having in a manner cut all the *Turkes* throates, some *Spanyards* shewed themselves upon the Decke, and called out a loud unto those whom they supposed to bee *Spanyards,* that they would come aboord them, and enjoy the reward of their victorie. *Ricaredo* asked them in *Spanish* what shippe that was? they told him that shee was a *Portugal* come from the *East-Indies* laden with spices, and as many Pearles, and Diamonds, as were worth a Million, and that by a storme they were driven upon that Coast, all rent and torne, and without any Ordnance, for the foulenesse of the weather, and high working of the Sea, inforced them to throw it over-boord. That their men were most of them sicke, and almost dead of thirst, and hunger; and that those two Gallies which were belonging to the Pirate *Arpantemuam* had taken her but the day before, without making any defence at all. And that (as it was told them) because they were not able to carrie so great a quantitie of riches in those two small Vessells; they towed her along, with purpose to put her into the River of *Larache,* which was neere thereunto.

Ricaredo returned them answere, that if they conceived that those his two Shippes were *Spanish,* they were deceived, for they were nothing lesse, but ships belonging to the Queene of the Northern Island. Which newes gave those that heard it, occasion of feare, and sorrow; imagining (and not without reason,) that they were fallen out of one net into another. But *Ricaredo* told them that they should receive no

harme, and that they should rest assured of their libertie, on condition that they should not put themselves upon their defence. Nor is it possible for us (replied they) so to doe; for (as wee formerly told you) this Shippe hath no Ordnance, nor wee any offensive Armes; and therefore wee must of force whether wee will or no, have recourse to the gentile and noble disposition of your Generall, and the liberalitie and courtesie which hee shall use towards us; since that it is meet and just that hee who hath freed us from the insufferable captivitie of the *Turkes,* should reape the reward and benefit thereof, and shall bee famoused of all those to whose eares the newes shall come, of this memorable victorie, and of his kinde usage towardes them.

These words of the *Spanyard* did not sound ill in *Ricaredo's* eares; and therefore calling those of his shippe to a councell, hee demanded of them how hee might send all the Christians to *Spaine,* without putting themselves in danger of any sinister successe; if being so many as they were, they should take courage unto them for to rise up against them? Some were of opinion, that hee should passe them one by one to his owne Shippe, and clapping them under hatches, kill them man after man; and so they might easily and without any noyse kill them all, and carry the great Shippe along with them to *Mundolin* without any further feare or care taking. But to this *Ricaredo* thus replied.

Since that God hath done us this so great a favour, in giving us such great riches, I will not requite him with a cruell and unthanke⁄full minde; nor is it meete that that which I may remedie by industry, I should remedie it by the sword. And therefore, I for my part am of opinion, that no Christian should dye the death. Not because I wish them so well, but because I wish well to my selfe, and would that this dayes noble action, neither to me, nor to you, should mingle the name of valiant, with the sir⁄name of cruell; for crueltie did never sort well with valour. That which is to bee done, is this; that all the Ordnance of one of these our Shippes, be put into the great *Portugal*

Ship, without leaving the Ship any Armes, or any other thing, save sufficient victuall. And so manning that Ship with our men, we will carry it home, and the *Spaniards* goe in the other to *Spaine*.

None durst contradict that which *Ricaredo* had propounded, and some held him to bee valiant, magnanimous, and of good under-standing and judgement; and others in their hearts, to be more courteous then he ought to have beene.

Ricaredo then having resolved on this course, he put 50. Muskatiers into the *Portugal* Ship all readie fitted and furnished, their Peeces charged with shot, and their matches burning in their cockes. He found in the Ship well neere 300. persons, with those that had escaped out of the gallies. He presently called for their Cocket, or bill of lading; and the same person who at first spake to him from the Decke made him answer; that the *Turkish* Pirate had alreadie taken their Cocket from them, and that it was drowned with him. Hee did instantly put his pully in order, and bringing his lesser vessell and lashing it close to the side of the great Ship with wonderfull celeritie, and with the helpe of strong ropes, they hoysed all their Ordnance with their Carriages, out of the lesser into the greater Ship.

This being done, hee forthwith made a short speech to the Chris-tians; he commanded them to goe into the Ship that was now dis-incumbred, where they should finde good store of victuall for more then a moneth, and more mouthes then they had. And as they went Imbarquing themselves, he gave to every one of them foure *Spanish Pistolets,* which he caused to be brought from his owne Ship, for to relieve in part their necessitie when they came on land; which was so neere, that from thence they might kenne the high mountains of *Avila,* and *Calpe.* All of them gave him infinite thankes for the favour he had done them; and the last that went to embarque himselfe, was he who had beene the mouth of the rest, who said unto *Ricaredo.*

Most valiant sir, I should hold it a happines for me, amidst these my misfortunes, and the greater of the two; that you would rather carry me along with you to *Mundolin,* then send me into *Spaine.* For albeit that it be my Countrey, and that it is not above six dayes since I left it, yet shall I not finde any thing therein which will not minister occasions unto mee of reviving my former sorrowes, and solitudes. I would have you to know (noble sir) that in the losse of *Cadiz,* which is now some 15. yeares since, I lost a Daughter which some of the Conquerours carried away into their owne Countrey; and with her, I lost the comfort of my old age, and the light of mine eies, which since they might not see her, have never seene that thing which could be pleasing unto them. The great discontentment wherein her losse left mee, together with that of my wealth, which likewise was taken from me; brought me to that low ebbe, that I neither would, nor could any more exercise the trade of Merchandize, whose great dealings in that kinde, made me in the opinion of the world, held to be the richest Merchant in all that Citie. And indeed so I was, for besides my credit, which would passe for many hundered thousands of crownes, the wealth that I had within the doores of mine owne house, was more then fifty thousand Duckets. All which I lost, yet had I lost nothing, so as I had not lost my Daughter. After this generall misfortune, and so particularly mine; necessitie (the more to vexe me) set upon me, never ceasing to give mee over, till such time as not being able any longer to resist her; my Wife and I (which is that sorrowfull woman that sits there) resolved to goe for the *Indies,* the common refuge of poore Gentlemen; and having embarqued our selves but sixe dayes since in a ship of Advise, we had no sooner put out of *Cadiz,* but that those two Vessells of the Pirates, tooke our shippe, and wee become their slaves. Whereupon our miserie was renewed, and our misfortune confirmed. And it had beene greater, had not the Pirates taken that shippe of *Portugal,* who entertained them so long, till that succeeded which you have seene.

22

Ricaredo then asked him, what was his daughters name?

He answered, *Isabella*.

With this *Ricaredo* ceased to be confirmed further in that which before he suspected; which was, that he who recounted this unto him, was his beloved *Isabella's* Father; and without giving him any tydings of her, he told him, that very willingly hee would carry him and his Wife to *Mundolin*, where happily they might heare some newes of that which they so much desired. He made them presently go aboord his own ship, leaving Marriners and souldiers sufficient in that of *Portugal*.

That night they hoysed sayle, and set themselves to get off from the coast of *Spaine*; and for that in the ship wherin were the freed Captives, there were likewise 20 *Turks*, whom *Ricaredo* had also set at libertie; for to shew, that more out of his owne noble disposition, and generous minde, he had dealt so graciously with them, then inforced by that love which he bare to the Christians; hee entreated the *Spanyards* at their parting, that upon the first occasion that should offer it selfe, they should set the *Turkes* at liberty, wherein they should shew themselves thankefull unto him.

The winde, which gave good tokens of being large, and prosperous, began to bee very much calmer, which calme did stir up a great tempest of feare in the Marriners and Souldiers; who blamed *Ricaredo*, and his bounty, not sticking to tell him, that they whom hee had freed, might give advise of their successe in *Spaine*; and that if happily they should have their Galeons lying there in the Haven, they might put forth to Sea in search of them, and so put them to a narrow streight, and in danger of losing, together with their lives, all that Treasure which they had got.

Ricaredo knew very wel that they had reason on their side, but over-comming all of them with good words, he made them quiet; but that which did most quiet them, was the winde which returned againe to re-infresh it selfe in such sort, that having as fayre a gale as could blow in the skie, they clapt on all their sayles, without having need to strike any one of them, or but in the least manner to restraine them; within Nine dayes they came within sight of *Mundolin*. And when they were returned home thus victorious, there were thirty wanting of those that went that Voyage.

Ricaredo would not enter the River with tokens of joy, by reason of the death of his Generall; and therefore mixed his joyfull, with sorrowfull signes. One while the Trumpets sounding loud, and shrill; and another while low, and hoarse; one while the Drummes did beat lively, and the Flutes goe merrily, and another while dead, and softly, answering each other with mournefull and lamentable notes. On one of the Cages of the shippe hung the contrary way, a flagge embroydered with halfe Moones; and on another, a long streamer of blacke Taffata, whose points did mocke the water.

In conclusion, with these and the like contrary extreams, they entered the River with their own shippe, because the other drew so much water, that the River could not beare her, and therefore lay at anchor in the Sea.

These such contrary signes and tokens, held a world of people in suspence, who beheld them from each side of the shoare. They knew very well by some Armes and Coats in their Colours, that that lesser shippe was the Admirall wherein the Lord of *Lansac* went; but they could not guesse how that other shippe should come to be changed for that great vast shippe which lay at Sea. But they were quickly put of this doubt, by *Ricaredo's* leaping out of his boat on shoare in rich and resplendent Armes, like a Souldier; who a foot, without staying for any other company, attended onely with the innumerable vulgar that followed him; he went directly to the Court, where the Queene being in a Gallerie, stood expecting the newes should be brought her of her ships.

There was, besides many other Ladies, with the Queen *Isabella,*

apparelled after the Island fashion, though with a little touch of the *Spanish.* Before that *Ricaredo* came, there came another, who told the Queene that *Ricaredo* was come. *Isabella* hearing the name of *Ricaredo,* began to change colour, and seemed to bee somewhat troubled, and in that very instant did feare and hope, both the evill and good successe of his comming.

Ricaredo was tall of stature, a gentleman, and well proportioned, and for that hee came Armed with his Gorget, Corselet, and Powderns, all *Millaine* worke, richly gilded and ingraven, it became him extreamely well, and did please the eyes of the beholders. He had no Caske on his head, but a broad brim'd hat of a Lyon colour, with a great large feather, diversified with a few different colours; a broad short sword by his side, a very rich girdle and hangers, and his breeches somewhat large, and full, like unto those of the *Swizzers.*

Being thus acoutered, what with the goodlinesse of his presence, and statelinesse of his gate; some were so taken therewith, that they compared him to *Mars* the god of Warre; and others taken with the beautifulnesse of his countenance compared him to *Venus,* who for to put a jeast upon *Mars,* had put this disguise upon him. In conclusion, he came before the Queene, and humbling himselfe on his knee, he sayd unto her.

Most renowned, and redoubted Soveraigne, in the strength of your good fortune, and in the consecution of my desire; after that our Generall the Lord of *Lansac* was dead of an Apoplexie, I succeeding in his place (thankes be rendered therfore to your Majestie) I lighted by chance on two *Turkish* gallies, which went towing away that great shippe which I have now brought home, and lyes not far off safe in the roade. I did set upon them, your Souldiers fought as they alwaies use to do, very manfully; we sunck both the *Turkish* Vessells, and in one of ours, I gave in your Majesties royall name libertie to the Christians, which escaped out of the hands of the *Turkes.* Onely I

26

brought along with me one man, and a woman, both *Spanyards*; who out of their owne liking and election, were wonderfully desirous to come with me into our Island, that they might see the greatnesse of your Majesties Person, and Court. That shippe which is now yours, is a *Portugal*, one of those great Carricks which come from the *East-Indies*, the which by a storme came to fall into the power of the *Turkes*; who with little trouble, or to say better, none at all, made her to yeeld her selfe unto them; and as I am informed by some of those *Portugals* that came in her, she is worth above a Million in gold, and Spice, and other rich Merchandize of Pearles, and Diamonds, which are in her, whereof nothing hath hitherto beene toucht, neither did the *Turkes* come to finger any thing therein; because Heaven hath dedicated it wholy unto you, and I have commanded it to bee kept and reserved whole and entire for your Majestie; which with one jewell onely that your Majestie shall be pleased to bestow upon mee, I shall remaine indebted for ten such other ships. Which jewell your Majestie hath alreadie promised mee, which is, my good *Isabella*. With her I shall rest rich, and rewarded; not onely for this service that I have done your Majestie, but for many other which I meane to doe, for to pay some part of that great, if not infinite worth, which in this jewell your Majestie offereth me.

Arise *Ricaredo* (replied the Queene) and beleeve mee, that if I should upon a price give you *Isabella* according to that valew I esteeme her at, you would never bee able to pay it, neither with that which you have brought home in this shippe, nor with all that treasure which remaineth in the *Indies*. Well, I will give her you, because I made you a promise of her, and because she is worthy of you, and you of her, your valour onely doth deserve her. And if you have kept those jewells of the Shippe for mee, I have likewise kept this your jewell for you. And albeit it may seeme unto you that I have not done any great matter for you, in returning you that which is your owne; yet

I know that I doe you an especiall favour therein; for those pledges that are bought by our desires, and have their estemation and value in the soule of the buyer, they are worth a World, there being no price that can countervaile it. *Isabella* is yours, there shee is; and when you will your selfe, you may take possession of her, and I beleeve with her good liking and content; for shee is discreet, and knowes well how to weigh the friendshippe which you doe her, for I will not style it by the name of favour, but friendshippe; for I will take that name onely upon mee of doing favours. Goe, and take your ease, and come and waite upon Vs to morrow, and then will I more particularly heare you relate unto Vs what you did in this Voyage, and how valiantly you behaved your selfe. And bring those two with you, who you say were so willing to come and see Vs, that We may thank them for their love.

Ricaredo thanked her Majesty for the many favours she had done him. And then the Queen presently left the Gallerie, and retyred her selfe. And the Ladies came round about *Ricaredo*; and one of them which held great love and friendship with *Isabella*, called the Ladie *Tansi*; accounted the discreetest, the wittiest, and pleasantest amongst them, sayd unto *Ricaredo*, what meanes this *Ricaredo*? what Armes are these? Did you happily imagine that you came to fight with your enemies? beleeve mee, wee all here are your friends, unlesse it be *Isabella*; who for that she is a *Spanyard*, is bound not to beare you any good will. Sure (my Ladie *Tansi*) shee beares mee some; for since that she hath mee in her remembrance (sayd *Ricaredo*) I know that her good will is towardes mee; for the foulnesse of being unthankefull, cannot have the least footing in her so great worth, understanding, and incomparable beautie.

Whereunto *Isabella* replied, *Signior Ricaredo*, since that I am to bee yours, it is in your power to take all satisfaction whatsoever you will of me, that I may make you some small requitall of those undeserved praises which you have given me, and of those further favours which you intend to doe me.

These and other the like honest discoursings, *Ricaredo* passed with *Isabella,* and with the rest of the Ladies; amongst which, there was a prettie little Damosell, young both in growth, and yeares, who did nothing but gaze upon *Ricaredo* all the while hee was there; shee lifted up his Bases, to see if hee had any thing under them; shee tampered with his sword, and in a Childish simplicitie, would make his glittering Armour her looking Glasse, comming very neere thinking to see her face in them. And when shee went away from him, turning her selfe to the Ladies, shee sayd; Now (Ladies) I assure you, I imagine that War is a most beautifull thing; since that even amongst Women armed men looke lovely. And how can they otherwise chuse? (replied the Ladie *Tansi*) if not, looke upon *Ricaredo,* who lookes like the Sunne, come downe from Heaven on earth, and in that habite goes walking up and downe amongst us. They all of them laughed at the little Maydes simplicitie, and no lesse at the ridiculous *Rodamantado* of the Ladie *Tansi.* And some murmurers were not wanting, who held it an impertinencie, that *Ricaredo* should come armed to Court. Though other some sought as much to excuse him, saying; that as a Souldier hee might doe it, for to show his braverie and gallantrie.

Ricaredo was by his Parents, friends, kinsfolke, and acquaintance received, with lively expressions of singular love and affection. And that night there were made generall bonfires throughout *Mundolin,* and other publick tokens of their joy. The father and mother of *Isabella* were alreadie in *Clotaldo's* house, whom *Ricaredo* had acquainted who they were; but entreated his Parents that they might not have any the least notice given them of *Isabella,* till that hee himselfe should give it them; the like advise was given to all the servants of the house.

That very night, accompanied with many boats, barges, and

29

barques, and with no fewer eyes to looke on them. The great Ship began to discharge her lading, which in eight dayes could not bee disburthened of her Pepper, and other rich Merchandize which she had in her bulke. The next day after *Ricaredo* went to Court, carrying with him the father and mother of *Isabella,* both of them being newly clad after the fashion of *Mundolin,* telling them that the Queene desired to see them.

They came all of them where the Queene was sitting amidst her Ladies expecting *Ricaredo,* whom she was willing to grace and favour, by placing *Isabella* next to her, having on the same attyre and dressing which shee wore when shee came first to the Court; appearing therein no lesse beautifull now, then shee did then. The Parents of *Isabella* wer strucken with admiration and wonder, to see so much greatnesse, and braverie met together. They setled their eyes on *Isabella,* but did not know her, though their hearts (presagers of that good which was so neere them) began to leape in their bosomes; not out of any sudden passion that might cause sorrow or grief in them, but out of I know not what pleasure and contentment, which they could not hit upon to understand aright.

The Queene would not suffer *Ricaredo* to continue kneeling before her, but made him rise, and willed him to sit downe in a velvet chayre, which was by her appointment set there for that purpose; an unusuall favour, considering the stately condition of the Queene. And one whispered in anothers eare, *Ricaredo* sits not on the chayre which was brought him, but on the Pepper which hee brought in. Another say's unto him that stood by him; now is that old Proverbe verified, *Que dadivas, que brantan pennas,* that *gifts will breake through stone walls;* for those that *Ricaredo* hath given her Majestie, hath softned and mollified our Queens hard heart. Another tells his next fellow, now that hee is well seated, more hands then two must go to it to heave him out.

In conclusion, from that grace and honour which the Queene was

31

pleased to doe *Ricaredo*; envie tooke occasion to grow in many of those Courtiers breaſts, who were eye-witnesses of this her Majeſties extra-ordinary favour extended towards him. For there is not that favour which a Prince confers on his Favourite, which is not a speare that pierceth the heart of the envious.

The Queene was desirous to know from *Ricaredo,* point by point, how that fight passed with the *Turkish* Pirates Gallies; hee recounted it a new, attributing the victorie to God, and the valour of his Souldiers; endearing the services of them all joyntly, and particularlizing the valiant acts of some of them, who had put themselves moſt forward, and done her Majeſtie very notable service; whereby he oblieged the Queene to doe all of them favours, and in particular, those particular persons.

And when he began to speake of the libertie which in her Maieſties name he had given the *Turkes,* and *Chriſtians,* hee sayd unto her. That Woman, and that Man who ſtand there (pointing to *Isabella's* Parents) are they whom yeſterday I told your Maieſtie, who out of the great desire which they had to see your greatnesse, and magnificence; did so earneſtly entreate mee that I would bring them along with mee. They are of *Cadiz,* and by that which they have told me, and by that likewise which I have seene and observed in them, I know that they are of especiall ranke, and worth.

The Queene commanded them that they should draw neere unto her; *Isabella* lifted up her eyes that shee might see these who sayd they were *Spainyards,* and more particularly of *Cadiz*; out of a desire that she had to learne if happily they knew her Parents. And juſt as *Isabella* lifted up her eyes, her Mother fixed hers upon her, and ſtood ſtill a while, that she might view and behold her the more attentively. And on the other side there began to be awakened in *Isabella's* memorie, some certaine confused notions, which gave her to under-ſtand, that heretofore she had seen that Woman which ſtood before

her. Her Father was in the like confusion, without daring to determine to give credit to that truth which his eyes represented unto him.

Ricaredo was very attentive to see and observe the affections and
motions of these three doubtfull and perplexed soules, which were so
confounded and amazed, between the yea and nay of knowing each
other. The Queen tooke notice of both their suspensions, as also of
Isabella's distractions, by her inter-while sweatings, by her changing
colour, and by her lifting up her hand to order and compose her hayre.

Isabella thus troubled, not knowing well what to thinke of it, did
earnestly wish that shee would speake, whom she imagined might be
her Mother; for peradventure her eares would put her out of that doubt
whereinto her eies had put her. The Queene willed *Isabella* that she
should speake *Spainish* to that woman, and that man; and they should
tell her what was the cause that moved them not to accept and enioy
that their libertie which *Ricaredo* had given them; being that libertie
is a thing above all other, the dearest and best beloved, not onely of
reasonable creatures, but of those that want it. All this *Isabella* demanded of her Mother, who without returning her any one word,
suddenly, and halfe stumbling for haste, came unto *Isabella*; and without regarding respect, feare, or the Courtiers looking on her, with her
hand she lifted up *Isabella's* right eare, and having there discovered
a black mole; which marke confirmed her suspition, and plainely
perceiving that it was her Daughter *Isabella*, she could no longer containe her selfe, but embracing her, cried out aloud, saying; Oh
Daughter of my heart! Oh deare pledge of my soule! and not being
able to utter a word more; her speech fayling, she fainted and fell into
a swound in *Isabella's* armes.

Her Father no lesse tender then prudent, gave manifest signes how
sensible he was of all this; but with no other words then a silent
shedding of teares, which softly trickling downe bedewed both his
cheekes, and beard. *Isabella* layd her face to that of her Mother, and

turning her eyes towards her Father, in such a kinde of manner looked on him, that thereby shee gave him to understand the pleasure and contentment her soule tooke in seeing them there.

The Queene wondering at this so rare and strange an accident, sayd to *Ricaredo*; I conceive (*Ricaredo*) that this interview was thus pre-ordered in your discretion; but I must tell you, I know not whether you did well in so doing. For we see by experience, that a sudden joy as soon kills, as a sudden sorrow. And having said this, she turned her selfe to *Isabella*, and tooke her apart from her Mother, who having a little water sprinkled in her face, came again to her selfe; and calling her wits a little better about her, humbling her selfe on her knees before the Queene, shee sayd unto her.

I beseech your Majestie to pardon my boldnes, for it is no mervaile that I should forget my selfe, and lose my sences, with the overmuch joy I have received in the finding out this my beloved pledge.

The Queene made answer, that she had a great deale of reason on her side (making use of an Interpreter that she might the better under-stand her.)

Isabella came in this manner (as I told you before) to the knowledge of her Parents, and her Parents of her; whom the Queene commanded to reside in the Court, to the end that they might with the better leisure, both see, and talke with their Daughter, and rejoyce and make merry with her. Wherewith *Ricaredo* was wonderfull well pleased, and craved anew of the Queene, that she would be pleased to make good her promise, by bestowing *Isabella* upon him, in case hee did deserve her; and if not, hee humbly besought her Majestie, that shee would bee pleased presently to put him upon some other employment, that might make himselfe worthie of obtaining that which he so earnestly desired.

The Queene understood very well, that *Ricaredo* rested well satisfied of himselfe, and of his great valour; insomuch that there needed not onely new proofes for to qualifie him. And therefore told him, that foure dayes from that present being fully ended, she would deliver *Isabella* unto him, doing both of them all the grace and honour she possible could. Vpon this answer, *Ricaredo* tooke his leave, being the most joyfull, and most contented man in the world; transported with that neere hope which hee now had of having *Isabella* in his power, without any feare of losing her, which is the last and utmost desire of Lovers.

Time ranne, but not with that light and nimble foot as hee wished. For they who live by the hope of promise to come; doe evermore imagine, that time doth not flye with wings swift enough, but that he hath lead tyed to his heeles, and treads the steps of slothfulnesse it selfe.

Well, at last came that desired day, not wherein *Ricaredo* thought to put an end to his desires, but to finde in *Isabella* new graces which might move him to love her the more, if more he could, then he did alreadie. But in that short time, when as he thought the shippe of his good fortune sayled with a prosperous winde towards the desired Port; a contrary chance, and crosse accident, raised up in this calme sea such a tempestuous storme, that he feared a thousand times to see it suncke.

The case then is this. The chiefe Bed-chamber Ladie to the Queene, to whose charge *Isabella* was committed; had a Sonne of the age of 22. yeares, called the Earle of *Arnesto*. The greatnesse of his estate, the noblenesse of his bloud, and the great favour which his Mother held with the Queene, made him not onely doe those things which did not become him, and to breake out into excesses; but also made him arrogant, proud, haughtie, and confident of himselfe.

This *Arnesto* then was enamoured of *Isabella*, and so enflamedly, that his very soule did burne in the sparkeling light of *Isabella's* eyes. And albeit in that time that *Ricaredo* was absent, he had by some signes discovered his desires; yet was he never admitted by *Isabella*, or received any the least incouragement. And howbeit that repugnancie, and disdaines in loves infancie, are wont to make lovers to desist from

35

their enterprize; yet in *Arnesto,* the many and knowne disdaines which *Isabella* shewed him, wrought the cleane contrary; for hee was set on fire with his owne jealousies, and burned with desire to attempt her honestie.

And for that he saw that *Ricaredo* in the Queens opinion had deserved *Isabella,* and that within so little a while she was to be given unto him for Wife, he was ready to runne into despaire, and to offer violence to himselfe. But before that he would goe about to use so infamous and cowardly a remedie, hee brake with his Mother, entreating her that she would speake unto the Queene to give him *Isabella* to bee his Wife; which if shee did not bring to passe, that he would then have her to know, and assuredly beleeve, that death stood knocking at the doores of his life.

The Mother wondred to heare such words fall from her Sonne, and for that she knew the roughnesse of his harsh nature, and headstrong condition, and the fastnesse wherewith these desires did cleave unto his soule, she was afrayd that this his love would end in some sinister successe, and unhappie issue; yet notwithstanding, as a Mother (to whom it is naturall to desire and procure the good of her Children,) shee promised to preferre his pretension to the Queene, though not with any hope to obtaine such an impossibilitie of her, as the breaking of her Princely word; but that shee might not omit to try in so desperate a case the utmost remedie.

And *Isabella* being that morning apparrelled by order from the Queene, so richly, that my Penne dares not presume to deliver the manner thereof unto you; and the Queene her selfe having put a chaine of Pearle about her necke, the best that was brought home by *Ricaredo* in the Shippe, valewed at twenty thousand Duckats; and a Diamond Ring on her finger worth sixe thousand or thereabouts. And the Ladies being assembled and met together for to celebrate the approaching feast of this glorious wedding, came in the chiefe Bed-chamber woman to the Queene, and besought her on her knees

EARL-ARNESTO

that shee would bee pleased to suspend *Isabella's* espousalls two dayes more. For with this favour onely which her Majestie should doe her, she should hold her selfe well satisfied and recompenced for all what-soever she deserved, or hoped for her service.

The Queene would first know of her why shee did so earnestly desire this suspension, which went so directly against her word, which she had given to *Ricaredo*. But that Ladie would not render her the reason, untill that she had granted her requeste, and that then shee would make it knowne unto her. The Queene longed to know the cause of that her demand. And therefore after that the Lady had obtained that which she much desired, shee recounted to her Majestie the love that her Son bare to *Isabella*; and how that she feared that if she were not given him to wife, he will either grow desperate to his utter undoing, or doe some scandalous act or other. And that whereas shee had craved those two dayes of delaying the businesse, it was only to this end and purpose, that her Majestie might have time to thinke upon some course, what might in her Majesties wisedome be most fit and convenient for her Sons good.

The Queene made answer, that if she had not past unto her her royall word, she would easily have found a way to get out of that laborinth. But that shee would neither breake her promise with her nor yet defraud *Ricaredo* of his hopes, for all the interest of the World.

This answer the Ladie of the Bed-chamber gave her Sonne, who flying instantly from his Mother, frying in the flames of love and jealousie, armed himselfe at all points; and being mounted upon a faire and strong limmed Horse, presented himselfe before the house of *Clotaldo*. And with a loud voice, requested that *Ricaredo* would come to the window that hee might speake a word with him; who at that instant was all in his gallantrie, like a bridegroome, and was even upon the point of going to Court, with such company as such a solemnitie required. But having heard a loud call, and being told who he was that called unto him, and in what kinde of fashion he came; being somewhat troubled with it, he came to the window; whom as soone as *Arnesto* saw, he sayd unto him.

Ricaredo, hearken well unto that which I shall now tell thee. My Mistresse the Queene commanded thee to goe forth in her service, and to doe such noble exploits as should make thee worthie of deserving, the not to be paralelled, incomparable *Isabella.* Thou didst goe, and returnedst with thy shippes laden with gold, wherewith thou thinkst that thou hast bought, and deserved *Isabella.* And albeit the Queene my Mistresse hath promised her unto thee; it was as being perswaded, that there was not any one in Court that hath done her better service, nor any that with better title may deserve *Isabella*; and herein it may very well bee that she was deceived. And therefore leaning to this opinion, which I hold for an approved truth, I tell thee; that thou hast neither done such things as may make thee to deserve *Isabella*; neither canst thou doe any which may be able to raise thee to so great a heighth of happinesse. And therefore in regard that thou nor doest, nor canst deserve her; if thou shalt avouch the contrary, I challenge thee the field, and defie thee to the death. And here the Earle ended his speech; and *Ricaredo* made answer thereunto after this manner.

This challenge (my Lord) doth in no manner of wise concerne mee; for I ingeniously confesse, that I not onely not deserve *Isabella*; but that there is not that man now living in the world that doth deserve her. So that I confessing that to be true which you say, this your challenge no way toucheth me; yet notwithstanding I accept of it, for that your insolencie, and indiscretion which you have showen in this your challenging of me.

And with this he withdrew himself from the window, and called in all haste for his Armes. This unexpected crosse accident much troubled his Parents, and all those that were come to *Clotaldo's* house, to accompany *Ricaredo* to the Court.

Amongst those many that had seene the Earle *Arnesto* armed, and had heard the challenge he had made; there were not some wanting who acquainted the Queen therewith. Who commanded the Captaine of her Guard that he should go presently and apprehend the Earle. The Captaine made such good haste, that he came just in the very nicke, when as *Ricaredo* was going out of his house, armed with those armes wherein he disimbarqued, being mounted on a goodly Horse.

When the Earle saw the Captaine of the Guard, he forthwith imagined the cause of his comming; and determined (if possibly he could avoyd it) not to be apprehended. And speaking aloud to *Ricaredo,* sayd.

Thou now seest (*Ricaredo*) the impediment which hinders us from deciding this quarrell. If (notwithstanding this interruption) thou shalt have a minde to chastise mee, thou wilt seeke after me; and I shall have the like minde to chastise thee, and seeke likewise after thee; and since two that seeke after each other, are easily found; let the execution of our desires surcease for the present.

Content, replied *Ricaredo*.

By this time the Captain was come in with all the Guard, and told the Earle that he must yeeld himselfe his Prisoner; for in her Majesties name he was to apprehend him. The Earle yeelded himselfe unto him; and told the Captain that he submitted himselfe to her Majesties Command; but with this condition, that he should not carry him to any other place, save the Queenes Presence.

The Captaine remained therewith satisfied, and carrying him in the midst of the Guard, brought him to Court before the Queene. Who had alreadie been informed by his Mother, of the great love which her Sonne bare to *Isabella*; and with teares besought her Majestie that shee would pardon the Earle, who being a young man, and deepely in love, was lyable to farre greater errours. *Arnesto* was brought before the Queene, who without entertaining any speech with him, commanded his sword to be taken from him, and afterwards sent him to Prison.

All these things tormented the heart of *Isabella*, as likewise of her Parents, who so suddenly saw the sea of their quietnesse troubled.

The Ladie of the Bed-chamber, *Arnesto's* Mother advised the Queene, that for to remove that mischiefe betwixt her house, and that of *Ricaredo*, that the cause thereof might be taken away; which was *Isabella*, by sending her into *Spaine*, and so those effects would cease, which now were to be feared.

Whereunto the Queen answered; that for the sending of her into *Spaine*, she should treate no more on that point; because her faire presence, and her many graces and vertues, gave her great content; and that doubtlesse, if not that very day, the next following, without all faile shee would marry her to *Ricaredo*, according to the promise she had made him.

With this resolution of the Queenes; *Arnesto's* Mother was so disheartened and discomforted, that shee replied not so much as one word. And approving that for good, which she had alreadie forecasted in her minde, that there was no other way, no other meanes in the world, for the mollifying of that rigorous condition of her Sonne, nor for the reducing of *Ricaredo* to tearmes of peace, save by taking away of *Isabella*. She determined to put in practise one of the greatest cruelties that could ever enter into the thought of any noblewoman, and especially so principall a one as she was. And this her determination was, to make away *Isabella* by poyson. And because it is commonly the condition of women to be speedy, and resolute in what they goe about; that very evening she gave *Isabella* poyson in a certaine Conserve, forcing her in a manner to take it, telling her that it was excellent good against those passions of the heart, wherewith shee seemed to bee troubled.

Having satisfied her importunitie, within a little while after that *Isabella* had taken it, her tongue and her throate began to swell, and her lippes to grow blacke, her voyce hoarse, her eies troubled, and her stomacke and bowells tormented with gripings; all manifest signes and tokens that she was poysoned.

The Ladies came to the Queene, acquainting her Majestie how it was with her; and certifying her, how that the Ladie of her Bed-chamber who had the charge of *Isabella,* had done her this ill office. There needed not much pressing to induce the Queene to beleeve that it was true; and therefore went presently to see *Isabella,* who was almost breathing her last.

The Queene commanded her Phisitians should be sent for in all haste, and in the meane while before they came, she caused a quantitie of the powder of *Vnicornes-horne* to be given her, and some other pre-servatives against poyson, which great Princes use alwaies to have readie at hand, upon the like cases of necessitie. The Phisitians came and applied their best remedies, and besought the Queene that shee would bee pleased to cause that Ladie of her Bed-chamber to make knowne unto them what kinde of poyson that was which she had given her; for it was not to be doubted that any other person but her selfe had poysoned her. She did discover what shee had given her; and having notice of it, the Phisitians applied so many and such effectuall remedies, that by them and Gods helping hand, *Isabella* remained with life, or at least in good hope of having it.

The Queene commanded her Bed-chamber woman to be appre-hended, and to be lockt up in a streight and narrow lodging in her Court, with intention to punish her according to the nature and qualitie of this her foule offence. Although that she sought to excuse her selfe by saying, that in killing *Isabella* she did sacrifice to the gods, by ridding the earth of a Christian; and together with her, removing the occasion of her Sonnes further quarrells.

This sad newes being brought to *Ricaredo*, made him almoſt out of his wits; such were the things he did, and such were the complaints he made.

In conclusion *Isabella* did not lose her life, yet the poyson had gotten that power over her, that she loſt the hayre of her head, and of her eye-browes, her face was ſtrangely pufft up, the graine of her skinne spoyled, her complexion marred, her whole body mightily swolne, and her eyes diſtilling watry humours. In a word, she was growne so foule and ill favoured; that she, who till then seemed to be a miracle of beautie, did now seeme to be a monſter of uglinesse. And they who knew her before, held it the greater misfortune of the two, that she remained in this evill plight, then if she had dyed of the poyson. Notwithſtanding all this, *Ricaredo* sued a new unto the Queene for her, and besought her Majeſtie that she would give him leave to carry her home to his house, because the love which he bare her, passed from his bodie to his soule; yet comforted himselfe with this, that though *Isabella* had loſt her beauty, yet could she not lose her infinite vertues.

Thou sayeſt true, replyed the Queene, goe take her home with thee *Ricaredo,* and make account that thou carryeſt with thee a moſt rich jewell in a course case. I would have given her as fayre to thee, as thou deliveredſt her unto me. But since this is not possible, forgive me that fault; happily the chaſtisement which I shall give to the committers of this foule offence, shall in part satisfie thy desire of revenge.

Many things did *Ricaredo* say unto the Queen, seeking to excuse the Ladie of her Bed-chamber, beseeching her Majeſtie to pardon her, since that the reasons she alleadged in her excuse, were sufficient for to move her to forgive her greater excesses then these.

In conclusion, *Isabella* and her Parents were delivered unto him, and *Ricaredo* carried them home, I meane to his Fathers house. To those rich Pearles, and that Diamond, the Queene added other jewells, and other changes of rayment; which were such, and so costly, that they discovered the great love which she bare to *Isabella,* who remained for the space of two moneths, without being able to be reduced to her former beautie. But the time being past, her skinne beganne to peele and fall away, and a fayre and smoothe graine of skinne to disclose it selfe.

In this interim, *Ricaredo's* Parents presuming that it was not possible that *Isabella* should become the same woman which heretofore she was; resolved to send for that Northern Damosell, with whom before that ever they treated with *Isabella, Ricaredo* (by agreement) was to marry. And all this they did without his knowledge, not doubting, but that the present beautie of this new bride, would blot out of his Sonnes remembrance, that of *Isabella,* which was now past; whom either they purposed to send into *Spaine,* together with her Father and Mother, giving them such store of wealth and riches, as should fully recom-pence their former received losses.

There passed not above a moneth and a halfe, when as without *Ricaredo's* privitie, the new spouse entred within his Fathers doores, accompanied like her selfe, very well, and so fayre and beautifull a creature, that next to *Isabella,* when she was in her prime, there was not the like unto her in all *Mundolin. Ricaredo* was mightily startled with the sudden and unexpected sight of the Damosell, and feared least the suddennesse of her comming, would put *Isabella* into some passion, and make an end of her life. And therfore, for to remove this feare, he went to the beds-side where *Isabella* lay; and finding her onely accompanied with her Father and Mother before them, he spake unto her after this manner.

Isabella of my soule; my Parents out of the great love which they beare unto mee, being not as yet well informed of that exceeding love which I still beare unto thee, have brought a Damosell into this house, with whom they have treated and concluded to marry mee,

44

before that I should know the worth that is in thee, or that thou shouldſt recover thy loſt health. And this they have done (as I verily beleeve) with intention, that the great beautie of this Damosell should blot thine out of my soule, which is therein so deepely engraven. I (*Isabella*) from the very inſtant that I lov'd thee, it was with another kind of love then that which hath its ayme, and end, in satisfying the sensuall appetite. For albeit, that thy corporall beautie did captivate my sences; yet thy infinite vertues were they which imprisoned my soule; so that if being fayre I did love thee, being now foule I adore thee. And for the further confirming of this truth, give me this hand, and she giving him her right hand, and he holding it faſt in his, prosecuted his speech, saying, By that faith which my Chriſtian Parents taught mee; and by that true God who heareth what we say, I promise thee (my deare *Isabella*) the one halfe of my heart, I vow my selfe thy Husband, and am so even from this very houre, if thou wilt rayse me to that heighth of happinesse to be thine.

Isabella remained in some suspence upon these words of *Ricaredo*, and her Parents amazed and astonished; she knew not what to say, nor doe any other thing, save her often kissing of *Ricaredo's* hand, and telling him with a voice intermingled with teares, that she accepted him for hers, and rendered her selfe to bee his servant. *Ricaredo* kissed that her foule face, which when it was fayre, he durst never presume to touch. *Isabella's* Parents with tender and many teares solemnize this nuptiall feast. *Ricaredo* told them, that he would put off his marrying with the Northerne Damosell which was now in the house, in such manner as he would hereafter give them to understand. And in case that his Parents should send all three of them into *Spaine*, that they should not decline it, but by all means get them goe; and that they should looke for him within two yeares, either in *Cadiz*, or *Sevilla*; assuring them in the word of a Gentleman, that ere that time were expired, hee would not fayle to bee with them, if Heaven should so long lend him life: and that if the time prefixed should be preterlapsed, they should then rest assured, that some great impediment or death, which was the more certaine, had crossed his intended journey.

Isabella made him answere, that shee would not stay onely two yeares for him, but all those of his life, till that she were truely certified, that he had left this life. And that, in that instant that this should come to her knowledge, the same likewise would be her death.

With these kinde words, fresh teares fell from them all. And *Ricaredo* went and told his Parents, that he would by no meanes be marryed, nor give his hand to the Northern Damosell to be his Spouse, till he had quieted his minde by a yeares travell. He knew well how to expresse himselfe, and gave them such good reasons for it; as likewise to the Parents that came with *Clisterna* (for that was the Damosells name) that being (as they were) all Christians, they did

46

easily give credit unto them; and *Clisterna* was contented to remaine in her Father in Lawes house, till *Ricaredo* should returne, who craved a yeares time.

This being thus concluded and greed upon, *Clotaldo* told *Ricaredo*, how that hee was resolved to send *Isabella* and her Parents to *Spaine*, if the Queene would give him leave so to doe. For (sayd he) peradven⸗ ture the ayre of her own Countrey will hasten and facilitate her health, which she now beganne to recover. *Ricaredo*, that he might not give any the least inckling of his designes, answered (though but coldly) his Father, that he should doe that which seemed best in his owne eyes; onely he besought him, that he would not take ought of those riches from *Isabella*, which the Queene had bestowed on her. *Clotaldo* promised he would not; and that very day hee went to crave license of the Queene, as well for the marrying of his Son to *Clisterna*, as for the sending of *Isabella* with her father and mother into *Spaine*.

The Queen was well contented with both his requests, and approved *Clotaldo's* determination. And that very day, without calling her Bed⸗chamber woman in question, She dismissed her of her service, and condemned her (besides the losse of her place) in ten thousand Crownes to *Isabella*. And the Earle *Arnesto*, for his challeng⸗ ing of *Ricaredo*, She banished him for six yeares. Foure dayes were scarce spent and gone, but that *Arnesto* was upon the point to go to cumply with his banishment, having alreadie taken order for the returning of his money.

The Queene commanded a rich Merchant to come unto her that dwelt in *Mundolin*, who had very good correspondencie in *France, Italy*, and *Spaine*; to whom She delivered ten thousand Crownes, and required of him bills of exchange, for the returning of them to *Isabella's* Father in *Sevilla*, or in any other part of *Spaine*. The Merchant dis⸗ counting his interrest and profit, told the Queene that he would make certaine and sure payment of them in *Sevilla*, by bills of exchange upon another French Merchant, his correspondent, in this manner and forme, *viz.* That hee would write to *Paris*, to the end, that the bills might bee made there by another correspondent of his, because they would accept and allow of those that came from *France*, but not from this Island; by reason of the prohibition of commerce betwixt those two Kingdomes, and that a letter of advice from him should serve the turne, by a privie marke that passed between them two; and that without any more adoe the Merchant of *Sevilla* should give him the moneys, who should bee advised thereof from *Paris*.

In fine, the Queene tooke such good securitie of the Merchant, that she made no doubt of the true payment of it. And not contenting her selfe with this, She sent for the Master of a Flemish shippe that lay in the River, and was to put forth the day following for *France*, onely to take testimonie thereof in some Port, that hee might bee the better able to passe into *Spaine*, under the title of comming from *France*, and not from the Island; whom shee earnestly entreated to carry with him in his shippe *Isabella*, and her Parents, and that hee should use them well and kindly, and land them in *Spaine* at the very first place hee should come at on that Coast.

The Master who desired to give the Queene contentment, told her that he would doe it, and that he would land them either in *Lisborne*, *Cadiz*, or *Sevilla*. Having taken sufficient securitie of the Merchant, and assurance from the Master; the Queene by way of message, sent unto *Clotaldo*, that he should not take any thing of that away from *Isabella* which She had given her, as well in jewells as in clothes.

The next day came *Isabella*, with her Father and Mother to take their leave of the Queene, who received them with a great deale of love. The Queene gave them the Merchants letter, and many other gifts, as well in money, as other curious dainties for their voyage. And *Isabella* with such courtshippe thanked her Majestie, that she left the Queene anew oblieged unto her, for to continue her favours still towards her. She tooke her leave likewise of the Ladies; who now that she was growne disfigured, would not that shee should have left them, seeing themselves free from that envie which they bare unto her beautie, and would have beene very well content to enjoy her gifts of wit, and discretion. The Queene embraced all three of them, and recommending them to their good fortune, and to the Master of the Shippe; and desiring *Isabella* to advertise Her, of her safe arrivall in *Spaine,* and from time to time, of her well-fare, by the way of the French Merchant; She tooke her leave of *Isabella,* and her Parents; who that very evening Imbarqued themselves, not without the teares of *Clotaldo,* and his Wife, and of all those of the House, of whom shee was extreamely beloved.

At this their taking of their leaves, *Ricaredo* was not present, who that hee might not make show of his tender heartednesse, and manifest his sorrow; procured some of his friends to goe abroad that day a hunting with him. The *Regalos* which the Ladie *Catalina* gave *Isabella* for her voyage were many, her embracings infinite, her teares in aboundance; her entreatings that shee would write often unto her, without number. And the thankes rendered by *Isabella* and her Parents, were answerable thereunto; so that though weeping, they left each other well satisfied.

That night the ship hoysed sayle, and having with a prosperous gale of winde touched upon the coast of *France*; and there taking in such provisions as were necessary for their voyage into *Spaine*; within 30. dayes after they entred the barre of *Cadiz,* where *Isabella* and her Parents dis-imbarqued themselves. And being knowne by all those of the Citie, they received them with expressions of much content. They received a thousand *parabienes* of the finding out of *Isabella,* and of the liberty which they had gotten, being first captivated by the *Moores,* and afterwards by the Northern Islanders. Having beene made acquainted with all the passages of that businesse, by those Captives whom the liberalitie of *Ricaredo* had set free.

Now *Isabella* in the meane while began to give great hopes of returning to recover her former beauty. They remained but a little more then
a moneth in *Cadiz,* refreshing themselves of their wearinesse in their
voyage; and then they went to *Sevilla,* for to see whether the payment
would prove good of the tenne thousand Crownes; which were to
bee put to the account of the French Merchant, who had undertaken
for to see it disbursed. Two dayes after their arrivall at *Sevilla,* they
enquired after him, and found him, and gave him the French Merchants letter, he did acknowledge the bill; but told them, that untill
he had received letters from *Paris,* and a letter of advise, hee could
not let them have the money, but yet that he looked every moment
to be advertised thereof.

Isabella's Parents had hyred a very fayre house, right over against
Santa Paula; by reason that there was a *Nunne* in that Monasterie, a
neere kinswoman of theirs, who had the only rare and sweetest voyce
in all *Spaine;* as well that they might be neere unto her, as also for that
Isabella had told *Ricaredo,* that if he should come to seeke her, he should
find her in *Sevilla;* and that her Cosen the *Nunne* of *Santa Paula* would
direct him to her house. And that for to know where to finde her, he
needed not to give himselfe any further trouble, then to enquire after
that *Nunne* which had the best voyce in the Monasterie, because this
token could not easily be forgotten.

It was forty dayes, before letters of advise came from *Paris,* and within
two dayes after they were come, the French Merchant delivered the
ten thousand Crownes to *Isabella,* and she them to her Parents; and
with them, and some other which they had got together, by selling
some of those many of *Isabella's* jewells; Her Father began again to
follow his trade of Merchandize, not without the admiration of those
who knew his great losses.

In conclusion, within a few monethes, he went repayring his lost
credit, and *Isabella's* beautie returned to it's former perfection. Inso-

much, that when any speech was had of fayre Women, all of them gave the Laurell to the North Isle *Spaniard*, who was as well known by this name, as she was for her beautie throughout the whole Citie.

By the order of the French Merchant of *Sevilla*, *Isabella*, and her Parents writ letters to the Queene of the North Isle, of their safe arrivall in *Spaine*; with such acknowledgments, and submissions at her Majesties feet, as the many favours from her received, did require. They likewise writ to *Clotaldo*, and to his Ladie *Catalina*, *Isabella* styling them her Father and Mother, and her father and mother them their lords. From the Queen they received no answer, but from *Clotaldo* and his Wife, they did; whom in their letters gave them the *parabien* of their safe arrivall. Certifying them besides, how that their Son *Ricaredo* the next day after that they had hoised saile, was gone for *France,* and from thence to passe to some other parts of Christendome, whether it was fitting for him to go, for the settling and securing of his conscience. Adding to these, other discourses and complements of much love, and affection, besides many other fayr and friendly offers. To which letters of theirs, they made answere with another, no lesse courteous and loving, then thankefull.

Isabella presently imagined, that *Ricaredo's* leaving his Countrey, was to come to seeke her out in *Spaine,* and feeding her selfe with this hope, she beganne to lead the most contented life in the world, and studied to live in such sort, that when *Ricaredo* should come to *Sevilla,* he might sooner heare the good report that went of her vertues, then come to the knowledge of her house. Seldome or never did she goe out of doores, unlesse it were to the Monasterie; she reaped no benefit by any other Iubilees, save those which she gained by the Monasterie. From her house, and from her oratorie, she went more with her meditations, then her feet. She never visited the River, nor walked to the *Triana*; she never went to see the common pastimes in the field *de Tablada*; nor to see the parts of *Xeres*; nor to goe if it were a fayre day, to the feast of Saint *Sebaſtia,* celebrated by so many people, as can hardly bee reduced to any number. But spent all her whole time in retyrednesse, in prayers, and good desires, ſtill looking for the comming of her *Ricaredo.*

This her great retyrednesse, did set on fire and inflame the desires, not onely of those young gallants of that ſtreet where she dwelt, but of all those that had but once had a sight of her. Hence grew night-musicke at her window, and day-careers with their *lennets.* And from this her not suffering her selfe to be seene, and from others much desiring to see her, encreased their seeking out of cunning Bawdes which were Miſtresses in their Art, and promised to shew themselves no lesse in soliciting *Isabella.* And there were not some wanting, who endeavoured to bring this their wicked purpose to passe by witch-craft, charmes, sorcerie, and the like lewd courses. But againſt all these, *Isabella* was like a rocke in the midſt of the Sea, againſt which the waves and the windes dash and beate, but doe not move it.

A yeare and a halfe was now paſt, when the approaching hope of those two yeares promised by *Ricaredo,* began with more earneſtnesse then hitherto it had done, to vexe and grieve the heart of *Isabella.* And whiles shee was now and then thinking with her selfe that her Husband was come, and that she had him before her eyes, and asked him what was the cause that hindered his comming, and had kept him so long from her. And while againe she imagined the juſt excuses that *Ricaredo* made her for his long absence, and how willingly she did beleeve, and receive them, and how lovingly shee embraced him in her armes, and hugged him in her bosome, as being the halfe part of her owne soule. Then, even then when she was thinking on these Love fancies, a letter came to her hands from the Ladie *Catalina,* bearing date from *Mundolin* some 50. dayes since. It was written in the tongue of the Island, but shee reading it in *Spanish,* saw that it spake thus.

Daughter of my soule, thou knowest very well *Guillarte Ricaredo's* Page, he went along with him in this his journey. And by a Former of mine unto you, I advertised you, that *Ricaredo* made for *France* the second day after your departure, and from thence was to travell farther. Now this his servant *Guillarte* at the end of sixteen moneths; in all which time, we had no newes of our Sonne, came home to us yesterday, and brought us these sad tydings, that the Earle *Arnesto* had by treacherie killed *Ricaredo* in *France*. Now then (Daughter) consider in what case his Father, my selfe, and his Spouse are in with this heavie newes; being such, I say, that they have not left us any hope of putting this our misfortune in doubt. That which *Clotaldo*, and my selfe entreate of you againe, and againe, is; that you will truely and earnestly remember *Ricaredo*, who well deserveth this good office from you, considering how dearely hee loved you, as you your selfe best know. You shall likewise begge of God, that hee will give us patience, and bring us to a good death; to whom wee likewise will make the same request; and humbly beseech him, that hee will give unto you, and your Parents, many long and happie yeares of life.

By the letter, hand, and seale, there was not any the least doubt left to *Isabella*, for not giving credit to the death of her Husband. She knew very well his Page *Guillarte*, and knew that hee was true and trustie, and that in his owne nature hee hated a lye, and that he had no reason in the World for to feigne that his death; and as little, his Mother Ladie *Catalina*; being that it imported nothing to send her such sorrowfull newes. In conclusion, no discourse that shee could make with her selfe, nothing that shee could imagine, could put it out of her thought, that this unfortunate newes was not true.

Having ended the reading of her letter without sheding a teare, and without shewing any signes of sorrow, with a composed countenance, and with (to appearance) a quieted and contented minde, she arose from the *Estrado* where she sate, and kneeling downe devoutly, she made a solemne vow to live a single life, since that shee might lawfully doe it being now a widow.

Her Parents dissembled their griefe, and covered that sorrow, with the cloake of discretion, which this sad newes had caused in them, that they might bee the better able to comfort *Isabella* in this bitternesse of her soule. Who being now as it were fully satisfied of her sorrow, moderating it with the resolution which shee had put on, she fell to comforting of her Parents, to whom shee discovered her intent. But they did advise her, that shee should not put it in execution, untill that those two yeares were over-past which *Ricaredo* had set downe for the tearme of his comming; for thereupon much depended the confirming of the truth of *Ricaredo's* death, and shee might then with the more safetie and securitie, change this her estate.

Isabella followed their counsell, and the six moneths and a halfe which remained for the accomplishing of the two yeares, she spent them in the exercises of a religious Damosell; and for the better preparing and fitting of her selfe for her entring into the Monastery, having made choice of that of *Santa Paula,* where her Cosen was.

The tearme of the two yeares was expired, and the day was come wherein shee was to take upon her the habit; the newes whereof was spred throughout the whole Citie, amongst those who knew her by sight, and by those that knew her onely by report. Now the Monastery stood not far off from *Isabella's* house; and her father inviting his friends, and they others, *Isabella* had one of the noblest and most honourable traines to accompany her thither, as in the like occasions was never seen in *Sevilla.*

There accompanied her the *Assistante,* the *Deane* of the Church, and the *Vicar-generall* of the *Arch-bishop,* and all the Ladies and gentlemen of title and qualitie that were in the Citie; so great was the desire that all of them had, to see that sunne of *Isabella's* beautie, which had so many moneths beene ecclipsed. And because it is the custome and fashion of those Damosells which goe to take the habit, to bee as gallant and as bravely adorned as possibly they can devise; who as one, that ever after from that instant sets up her rest, and takes her leave and farewell of all braverie, and wholy discards it. *Isabella* was willing (that she might not breake so ancient a custome) to tricke and set forth her selfe in the best and most curious manner that possibly she could invent. And therefore she did put on that gowne and kirtle, and those rich dressings which she had on when shee went to Court, which we have heretofore told you, how rich, how sightly, and how magnificent it was. There came forth to publicke view, those orient Pearles, and that glittering Diamond, with the Carkanet, chaine, and girdle, which likewise were of great valew.

Isabella went out of her house on foot, for her being so neere unto the Monasterie, excused Coaches, and Caroches. The concourse of the people was so great, that it repented them that they had not taken Coach, for they would not give them way to get to the Monasterie. Some blessed her Parents, others Heaven that had inriched her with so much beautie; some did stand on tiptoe for to see her, others, having seene her once, ranne to get afore, that they might see her againe.

But he that shewed himselfe most solicitous in this kind, and so much, that many tooke notice of him for it; was a man clad in one of those habits which they weare, who returne home redeemed from their Captivitie. This Captive then at that very time that *Isabella* had set one foot within the Porch of the Covent, whether were come forth to receive her (as the use is amongst them) the *Prioresse,* and the *Nuns;* with a loud voice he cried out, stay *Isabella,* stay; for whilest that I shall be alive, thou canst not enter into any Religious order. At the hearing of these words, *Isabella* and her Parents looked backe, and saw that cleaving out his way through the thickest of the throng, that Captive came making towards them; whose blew round bonnet being fallen off, which he wore on his head, he discovered a confused and intangled skeine of golden wyered hayres, curling themselves into rings, and a face intermixed with crimson, and snow, so pure red and white was his complexion; all of them assured signes and tokens, inducing all of them to take, and hold him to be a stranger.

In effect, one while falling through too much haste, and then getting him up quickly againe, he came at last where *Isabella* was; and taking her by the hand, sayd unto her. Knowest thou me *Isabella*? looke well upon me; behold, that I am *Ricaredo* thy Husband. Yes, I know thee (replied *Isabella*) if thou art not a phantasma, a walking spirit, or some false assumed apparition, that is come to disturbe my repose. Her Parents drew neerer and neerer unto him, and did view and eye him very narrowly; and in conclusion, came certainely to know that this Captive was *Ricaredo*; who with teares in his eyes, falling downe on his knees before *Isabella*, besought her that the strangenesse of that habite wherein she now saw him; might not be a barre to her better knowledge of him; nor that this his meane and baser fortune, should be a hinderance to the making good of that word and faithfull promise, which they had given and plighted each to other.

Isabella (maugre the impression which *Ricaredo's* Mothers letter had made in her memorie, sending her the newes of his death,) chose rather to give more credit to her eyes, and the truth which she had present before her, then to trouble her selfe to make a further needlesse inquirie. And therefore kindely embracing the Captive, she sayd unto him. You doubtlesse (sir) are the man who can onely hinder my determination; since that you are truely my husband, you can be no lesse then the better halfe of my soule. I have thee imprinted in my memorie, and have layd thee up in my heart. Come therefore (sir) unto my Fathers house, which is yours; and there I will deliver up unto you the possession of my person.

All these words the standers by heard, together with the *Assistante*, the *Deane*, and the *Arch-bishops* Vicar-generall of *Sevilla*. At the hearing whereof, they were all of them strucken with admiration, and stood a while as men astonished; and were desirous that it might presently be told them, what history this, and what stranger that was, and of what marriage they treated. Whereunto *Isabella's* father made answer, saying; that that historie required another place, and some time for to tell it. And therefore besought them, since that they were so willing to know it; that they would be pleased to returne backe with him to his house, being that it was so neere, and that there it should be recounted unto them, and in such a manner, that with the truth thereof they should remaine satisfied, and at the strangenesse of that successe, amazed.

This was no sooner sayd, but that one of those there present, spake aloude, saying, Gentlemen, this young man is a great Pirate, for I know him well enough; and that is he, who some two years since, and somewhat more; tooke from the Pyrates of *Argiers,* that ship of *Portugal,* which came from the *Indies.* Ye need not doubt that this is the man, for I confidently tell you that I know him; for he gave me my liberty, and money to bring me home to *Spaine*; and did not onely free me, but 300. Captives more, furnishing them with victualls, and moneys. With these words the vulgar were in an uproare, and the desire afresh revived, which all of them had to know and see such intricate things as these to be fully cleared.

In fine, the Gentlemen of more especiall ranke and qualitie, with the *Assistante,* and those two principall Churchmen, returned backe to accompany *Isabella* to her house, leaving the *Nuns* sorrowfull, and weeping, that they had lost so fayre a Sister, and companion as *Isabella.* Who being come home, and having brought the Gentlemen into a spacious large Hall, entreated them to sit downe; and albeit *Ricaredo* was willing enough to take upon him the relating of this desired history; yet notwithstanding it seemed good unto him, rather to trust *Isabella's* tongue and discretion with it, then his owne, who did not

I

very perfectly speake the language of *Spaine*. All that were present were in a still silence, and having their eares and soules readie prepared to heare what *Isabella* would say, she began to recount the story; Which I reduce briefly to this; that she delivered all that unto them, which happened from the day that *Clotaldo* by stealth carried her away from *Cadiz*, till her returne thither againe. Not omitting the battell which *Ricaredo* fought with the *Turks*, and the liberality and bountie which he had used towards the Christians, and the faith which both of them had plighted each to other, to be man and wife. The promise of two yeares, the newes which she had received of his death; and that so certaine to her seeming, that it put her into that course which they had so lately seene, of professing her selfe a *Nunne*. She did endeare the Queene of the North Islands bounty towards her, and the Christianity of *Ricaredo*, and his Parents. And ended her speech, with desiring *Ricaredo* that he would relate what had befallen him, from the time that hee left *Mundolin*, untill this very present; wherein they saw him clad in the habit of a Captive, and with a badge in his brest, betokening that he was redeemed by way of Almes.

It is true as you say, replied *Ricaredo*; and in a few short words, I will summe up unto you my many and great troubles. After that I went out of *Mundolin* for to excuse the marriage which I could not make with *Clisterna*, with whom *Isabella* told you my Parents would have mee to marry, taking *Guillarte* along with me; that Page, who (as my Mothers letters made mention) brought the newes to *Mundolin* of my death. Crossing *France*, I came to *Rome*; where of those two thousand Crownes which I had in gold, I delivered a thousand and sixe hundred to a Banker, who gave me a bill to receive so much in this Citie, upon one *Roqui* a *Florentine*. And with those 400 which remained with me, with intention to come for *Spaine*, I made for *Genoa*; whence I had notice given me, that there were two Gallies of that *Signorie* to goe for *Spaine*.

I came with *Guillarte* my servant, to a certaine Towne called *Aquapendiente*. And in an Inne where I alighted, I found the Earle *Arnesto,* my mortall enemie; who with foure servants went disguised, and went (as I conceive) to *Rome,* I did verily beleeve that he had not knowne me, I shut my selfe up in my lodging with my servant, and there kept my selfe close, and with a great deale of care and vigilancie, and with a determination and purpose, at the shutting in of night to get mee gone, and to change that my lodging for a safer. But I did not doe it, because the great carelesenesse which I observed in the Earle, and his followers, did assure me that he did not know me. I supt in my lodging, I made fast the doore, stood upon my guard with my sword in my hand; I recommended my selfe to God, and would not that night goe to bed. My selfe and my servant lay downe on a bench to take a little rest and sleepe, and my selfe was halfe fallen a sleepe.

But a little after midnight, they awakened me with purpose to make me sleepe an eternall sleepe. Foure pistolls (as I afterwards understood) the Earle and his servants discharged against me, leaving me for dead; and having their horses already in a readines, they presently put foot in stirrop and went away; bidding the Host of the Inne, that hee would see me fayrely buried, for that I was a man of principall note and qualitie. My servant (as mine Host afterwards told mee) awakened with the noyse, out of very feare leapt downe from a window, that looked out into a base Court, crying out; oh miserable and unfortunate that I am! they have slaine my Lord and Master; and having sayd this, he hyed him out of the Inne, and that with such feare, and haste, that he did not so much as looke backe, or make any stay till he came to *Mundolin;* so that it was he who brought the newes of my death.

They of the Inne got up, found mee shot athwart my bodie with foure bullets, and wounded with many other lesser shot; but all of them lighting on such parts, that there was not one mortall wound amongst them all. They cured me, but it was two moneths and better, before I was able to travell.

At the end whereof, I came to *Genoa,* where I found no other passage, save in two small boats, which my selfe, and two other principall *Spanyards* hyred; the one to goe before as a Vessell of advise

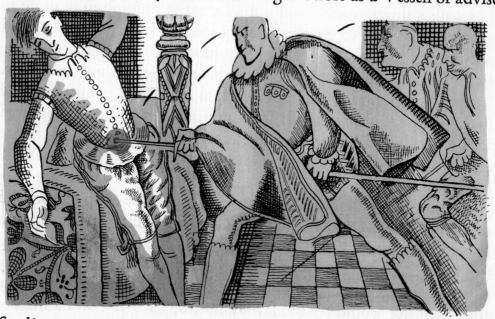

for discoverie, and the other we went in our selves. With this securitie, we embarqued our selves: sayling along the shoare, with intention not to ingulfe our selves; but comming over against that place which they call *Las tres Marias,* or the three *Maryes,* which is on the Coast of *France.* Our first boat going forward to see if she could discover any thing; in an unluckie houre, two *Turkish* Gallies that lay lurking there in a little creeke of the Sea under the Rockes; and the one of them putting her selfe forth to the Sea, and the other keeping close by the land; when they saw our drift that we meant to run a shoare, we were prevented in our course, taken by the *Turkes,* and stript of all that we had even to our naked skins. They rifeled the boats of all that they had, and suffered them to run a shoare, without offering to sincke them, saying; that they would serve another time to bring them another *Galina,* (for by this name they call those spoyles and booties which they take from the Christians.)

Yee may very well beleeve me, if I tell you that I felt in my soule the sorenesse of my captivity; and above all, the losse of those certificates, and provisions I received at *Rome,* which I brought along with mee, lapt up in a little boxe of plate; as likewise my bill of exchange for a thousand and sixe hundered Crownes. But as good lucke would have it, they lighted into the hands of a Christian Captive a *Spanyard,* who kept them safe; for if they had once come to the *Turkes* fingering, I should at least have given for my ransome, as my bill made mention of. They brought mee to *Argiers,* where I found the Fathers of the order of the blessed *Trinatie,* treating of the redeeming of Christian Captives; I spake with them, I told them who I was; and moved out of charitie, though I was a stranger unto them, they redeemed mee in this forme and manner following. They gave for mee three hundered Ducats, one hundred to be layd downe presently; and the other two, at the next returne of the Shippe that should come to redeeme the Father of that society, who remained in *Argiers,* engaged in foure thousand Ducats more then those that hee brought with him; for to such great pittie and compassion extended the charitie of these men, that they give their owne, for other folks liberty, and remaine themselves Captives, for to free others from Captivitie. And for an addition of this happinesse of my libertie, I found my lost boxe, with my certificates, and my bill also of Exchange. I shewed it to that holy Father who had ransomed me; and I offered him five hundered Ducats more then my ransome came to, towards the payment of his engagement.

It was almost a yeare ere the Shippe of almes returned; and that which in the interim happened unto mee, if I should goe about to recount it now unto you, it would be another new Historie. Onely I will tell you that I was knowne of one of the 20. *Turkes* whom I had set at libertie, with the rest of the Christians before mentioned. But he was so thankefull, and so honest a man, that he would not discover me. For had the *Turkes* knowne that I was the man that suncke their two Gallies, and tooke out of their hands that great shippe of *India*; they would either have presented me to the great *Turke,* or have taken away my life. And to have presented me to the great *Turke,* had been the losse of my liberty during life.

In conclusion, the father that did ransome me, came to *Spaine* with me, together with other 50. redeemed Captives. In *Valencia* we made a generall procession, and from thence every one went his owne way which he liked best, with these ensignes and tokens of their liberty, which are these poore kinde of habits. This day I came to this Citie, with so great and earnest a desire to see my espoused *Isabella;* that without any other thing detaining mee, I enquired for this Monastery, where I was to have notice given me of my Spouse. That which herein hath befallen mee, ye have alreadie seene; that which remaineth to bee seene, are these certificates in the plate-boxe which I told you of; and with that hee put them into the *Deanes* hand, who preserved them together, with the *Assistante,* who did not finde any thing in them, that might make doubt of the truth of that which *Ricaredo* had delivered unto them. And for further confirmation thereof, Heaven had so ordained it, that the *Florentine* Merchant was present at all this, upon whom the bill was for the payment of 1600. Duckats; who entreated that they would let him see the bill; and they shewing it him, he presently acknowledged, and accepted it, for it was many moneths since that hee had order for it. All this was but to adde admiration to admiration, and amazement to amazement.

The *Assistante* embraced *Ricaredo,* and *Isabella's* Parents, and her selfe; all of them in very courteous language offering them their service.

The like did the two Clergie men, and entreated *Isabella* that shee would set downe this storie in writing, that the *Arch-bishop* might reade it, which she promised she would. The people from the highest to the lowest giving the *parabien* to *Isabella, Ricaredo,* and their Parents, they tooke their leaves. And they on the other side besought the *Assistante,* that he would honour their wedding with his presence, which some eight dayes hence they did purpose to celebrate. The *Assistante* was very well pleased with the motion; and within eight dayes after, accompanied with all the highest and principall persons of the Citie, he wayted on them to Church.

By these turnings and windings, and by these circumstances, *Isabella's* Parents recovered their Daughter, and were restored to their former wealth; and she assisted by her many vertues, in despight of so many inconveniencies, lighted on a husband, of such especiall ranke and qualitie as *Ricaredo.* In whose company (it is sayd) she still liveth in that house which they rented right over against *Santa Paula,* which since they bought of the heyres of a gentleman of *Burgos,* called *Hernando de Cifuentes.*

This Novell may teach us, what great power vertue, and beautie have, since that both of them together, and each of them by themselves are of force, to make even their enemies in love with them. As likewise how that heaven knowes from the greatest adversities and afflictions, to draw the greatest benefits, and comforts.

THE JEALOUS HUSBAND

IT is not many yeares since, that out of a certaine Towne in *Estremadura*, issued a Gentleman borne of noble Parents; who like another Prodigall, through divers parts of *Spaine, Italy,* and *Flanders,* went spending and wasting as well his yeares, as his wealth. And in the end, after his many perigrinations, and travells, (his Parents being alreadie dead, and his patrimonie consumed;) he came at last to reside in the great Citie *Sevilla,* where he found sufficient occasion to waste and consume that little of his substance which he had left.

Now seeing himselfe in some want of moneys, and not having many friends, he had recourse unto that remedie whereunto many other decayed persons, and such as are broken in their estates commonly have recourse. To wit, to goe for the *Indies,* the refuge and protection of all your unthrifts, and desperate people of *Spaine,* the sanctuary of Banker-rupts, the safe conduct of murtherers, the cloake and cover for your cunning gamesters, to whom some give the name of cheaters; the common lure whereunto your looser women stoope, the generall deceiving of many, and the particular relieving of few.

In conclusion, comming thither in that time, and just as it were in the very nicke when as the Fleet was putting forth to sea, to make for the *West-Indies,* or *Tierra-Firme* (as the *Spanyards* call it) having agreed with the Admirall thereof, (upon what tearmes and conditions I know not) hee furnished himselfe with all such necessarie sea provisions as were fitting for so long a voyage; and having sent them aboord, embarqued himselfe at *Cadiz,* bidding *Spaine* farewell. They weighed anker, and with a generall joy (having as faire a winde as heart could wish) they hoysed saile, and it was not long before they had lost the sight of land, and found themselves prosperously ploughing the waves in those spacious plaines of that Grandfather of waters, the vast Ocean.

This our thoughtfull passenger revolving in his minde, and calling to his remembrance the many and diverse dangers which in those former yeares of his travells hee had passed, and the ill courses which he had taken throughout the whole course of his life, and what an ill governed yong man he had beene; having fallen into this account with himselfe; and seing what a bad reckoning he was like to make of it, did put on a firme and constant resolution to change his former course of life, to turne over a new leafe, and to alter his wonted style in spending, and to looke a little better then heretofore he had done, to that wealth and meanes which God should be pleased to bestow upon him, and to proceed with a little more warinesse and circum-spection then hitherto he had in those his loose and expencefull entertainments of women.

The Fleet was in a manner becalmed, when *Feli pede Carrizales* (for that is his name who ministers occasion of matter to this our story) had this storme and tempest within himselfe. Well, the winde re-turned to take new breath, putting the ships forward with such force and violence, that they left no man surely setled in his place. And therefore *Carrizales* was inforced to leave his imaginations, and to suffer himselfe to be carried away with those cares onely, which this his voyage offered unto him; which was so successefull, that without receiving any bylets, or hinderances, they happily arrived at the Port of *Cartagena.*

And for to let passe all that which maketh not for our present purpose; I say that when *Felipe* went for the *Indies,* hee was 48. yeares old. And in those 20. ensuing years whil'st he remained there; by his industry and diligence, hee grew to bee worth a hundered and fifty thousand Ducats.

Now then, seeing himselfe in so rich and plentifull an estate, touched with that naturall desire which all men have to returne home to their owne native Countrey, not regarding the great proffers, both for his private profit, and his publicke preferment which were offered him. Leaving *Peru,* where hee had gotten such great store of wealth bringing it along with him, all in barres of gold and silver, and seeing it registred, for to quit all inconveniencies, hee returned for *Spaine,* landed at S. *Lucars,* and came unto *Sevilla,* as well laden with yeares, as wealth. What hee brought thence appropriated to himselfe, at the unlading of the Galleons he had quiet possession given him, without any the least disturbance or interruption of officers. He inquired after his friends, and found them all dead; he had a great minde to goe to his owne Countrey, though he had already received newes that death had not left him any one kinsman alive.

And if when he went for the *Indies* poore and necessitated, many thoughts troubled his braines, not suffering him to be at quiet one minute of an houre in the midst of the waves of the Sea, no lesse did they now vexe him being on land, though the cause were different; for then he could not sleepe for thinking on his poverty, he could not now take any rest for thinking on his wealth. So heavie a loade is riches to him that hath not beene acquainted therewith, nor knowes not how to use them, as poverty is to him who lives in continuall want. Gold brings cares with it, and cares oppresse him who wants it; but the one are remedied by having some moderate quantitie thereof; and the other augmented, by having too much of it.

Carrizales his minde did runne often upon his wedges of gold, and did as often eye them, but not that he was miserable; because in those few yeares wherein he had beene a Souldier and followed the warres, he had learned to be free, and liberall; but what he should doe with them, because for to keepe them still in their being, would be altogether unprofitable; and to keepe them at home in his house, would be but a bayte for the covetous, and a tempting prey for theifes.

The desire of returning to the troublesome and unquiet trade of merchandize for the gaining of more wealth, was wholy dead in him; and considered with himselfe, that being of those yeares that he was, he had money more then enough to maintaine him well and plenti-

fully, during the remainder of those dayes that he had to live.

Otherwhiles, he was minded to carry it with him into his owne Countrey, and to put it out to profit, spending therein the yeares of his old age in rest and quietnesse, giving unto God that which he could, since that he had given to the World more then he should.

On the other side, he be- thought himselfe of the scarcity and poverty of his owne Coun- trey, and that the people round about him were very poore and needy; and that for to goe to live there, was but to make himselfe the Butt, and marke of all those importunities which the poore doe commonly give the rich, who is neere neighbour unto them; and more especially, when there is no other in that place, to whom they may repaire for the relieving of their miseries.

Againe, hee would feigne have one, to whom hee might leave his wealth after his owne dayes were ended. This desire running often in his head, and having now taken fast hold on him; he consulted with his owne strength, finding himselfe (to his seeming) able enough to undergoe and beare that heavie yoake of wedlocke. But hee had no sooner entertained this thought of Matrimonie, but instantly such a great feare came upon him; that as a Cloud is scattered and driven away by the winde, so vanished this his thought. For in his owne naturall disposition, hee was the most jealous man in the world, though being as yet unmarried; and now with onely the bare imagina-tion of being a married man, jealousies began to offend him, suspicions to trouble him, and strange fancies to vexe and torment him; and with such great effecacie and vehemencie, that hee was now quite off the hinges, and fully resolved with himselfe never to Marrie.

And having put on this resolution, but not being resolved what course to runne, or what manner of life to leade; his fortune had so ordained it, that passing one day along the streete, he should cast up his eyes, and see a Damosell standing in a window; being to his seeming about thirteene or fourteene yeares of age, being of so pleasing a countenance, and so fayre and beautifull, that good old *Carrizales* being not able to defend himselfe any longer; yeelded up the weake-nesse of his many yeares to those few of *Leonora*, (for this was the name of that beautifull Damosell.) And presently without any further de-tention, hee began to heape discourse upon discourse, and talking with himselfe, sayd.

This yong mayden is very faire, exceeding hansome, and very well favour'd, and by the outward shew which this house makes, I con-ceive they are none of the richest that dwell therein; she is young, her tender yeares may secure my suspicions; I will marry her, shut her up close, and mold her to my minde; by which meanes she shall not come to have any other condition, save that which I my selfe shall teach her. I am not so old, that I should lose the hope of having Children to inherit my estate; whether she bring a dowrie with her or no, it mattereth not, neither make I any reckoning of it, since that Heaven hath dealt so liberally with me, that I have (if enough be enough) enough and to spare. And such as are rich, ought not in their marriages to seeke after wealth, but their owne liking and con-tent, for this lengthneth mans life; whereas the contrary is the bane of wedlocke, and shortens the dayes of those that are so coupled together. No more I say, the Die is cast, and this is the chance which Heaven hath given mee.

And having this soliloquie with himselfe, not once, but a hundered times over and over. After some few dayes were over-past, he had speech with the Parents of *Leonora*, and came to know that though they were poore, yet were they of a noble Familie; and giving them an account of his intention, and of the qualitie of his person, and means; he entreated them to give him their Daughter to wife. They required time of him for to informe themselves of that hee had delivered unto them; and that hee likewise should do the like, for the better assuring himselfe of the truth of their noblenesse.

So for the present they parted; and the parties having well informed themselves each of other, they both found what they had sayd to be true. And so in conclusion, *Leonora* came to be the Spouse of *Carrizales*; having first endowed her with twenty thousand Ducats, so hotly was the heart of this jealous old man, set on fire with the love of *Leonora*. Who had scarce given his hand to be her Husband, but that on the sudden a troope of raging jealousies set upon him, and began without any cause given him, to shake and tremble, and to be afflicted with more and greater cares, then ever he had beene troubled with heretofore.

And the first manifestation which he made of his jealous condition, was; that he would not suffer a Taylour to take measure of those many changes of garments which hee was minded to make for this his young wife. And therefore went eying, if hee could meet with any other woman that was little more or lesse of the same size and stature, answerable to that of *Leonora*; at last he lighted on a poore Mayd, neere about her pitch; causing a Taylour that was a very good workeman, to take measure of her, and to make one whole sute fitting to her bodie; that done, bringing it to his wife, he wished her to put

it on; she did so. In fine, hee found that it did fit her to a hayre; and thereupon, according to that measure, hee caused the rest of her cloathes to be made; which were so rich, and so many, that the Parents of the espoused, held themselves exceeding happie, in having lighted upon so good a Sonne in Law, both for their owne, and their Daughters better good and maintenance.

The yong married wife was much amazed, wondring to see such a deale of gallantry; because in all her life before, her best weare was a gowne of Rash, and a Taffata-Kirtle.

The second token of his jealousie was, that hee would not bed his wife, till hee had brought her home to his owne house, which hee had ordered in this forme and manner. He bought one, which cost him Twelve thousand Ducats, being seated in a most principall place of the Citie, with a curious Garden belonging unto it; in the midst whereof was a fountaine, beautified round about with Grapes, Oranges, and Lemmons; diversified with sundry sorts of flowers, and fruits pleasing to the eye, and pleasant to the taste. He dammed up all the windowes that looked out towards the streete, and had no other light, but what the rooms received over head from Heaven. The like course he tooke with all the rest in his house. In the Portall of the streete (which in *Sevill* they call *Casa-puerta*) he made a stable for one Mule, and over it he built a little Tallet, or Hay-loft, with a lodging chamber joyning close to it, where he was to lye and make his abode, who had the charge thereof, being an old *Negro,* and an Eunuch. He raysed up his walls to a great heigth, leaving the roofe open; so that he whosoever hee were that entred into the house, must behold Heaven by a direct line, without being able to see ought else. Hee made a Tornill (such as your *Nunnes* have in their Monasteries) which from the *Casa-puerta,* or open Portall, did butt upon the inner Court. He had bought very rich houshold-stuffe wherewithall to adorne his house; so that for hangings, Carpets, Canopies, Chaires,

Stooles and all other utensills, all was Lord like, costly, and substantiall.

He bought likewise foure white female slaves, and burned them with a hot yron in their cheekes and forehead, setting his marke upon them; and other two *Blacke-Moore* she slaves, who knew no other language but their owne, save a little broken *Spanish*. He covenanted with a certaine Caterer, to buy and bring him in his houshold provision for his dyet; but with this condition, that he should not lodge in the house, nor enter thereinto no further then the Tornill, where hee was to deliver in what hee brought.

This being done, he put out part of his moneys to use, in good and sure hands; and part of it in banke, reserving a good round summe to lye still readie by him upon all occasions that should offer themselves unto him. He also caused one master-key to be made for all the whole house, and did locke up under that, all that whatsoever he did buy in grosse and in their due seasons, for the provision of the whole yeare.

And having thus ordered and disposed all things according to his owne minde, he went to his Father in lawes house and demanded his wife. Her Parents delivered her up unto him; with not a few teares, because it seemed unto them that they carried her to her grave. Tender hearted *Leonora,* both in heart, and yeares knew not as yet what had happened unto her; and so weeping for companie with her Parents, she craved their blessing; and taking her leave of them, attended by her slaves and servants, her Husband lending her his arme, led her home to his house.

Whereinto he was no sooner entred, but *Carrizales* made a speech unto all his servants; recommending the guard of *Leonora* to their charge, willing them that in no hand they should admit any one to enter within the second doore, no not the *Negro,* though an Eunuch. And she to whom more especially he recommended the keeping and cherishing of *Leonora,* was a Beldame of much prudence, and gravitie;

L

whom he had entertained to be as it were a governesse to *Leonora,* and a superintendent, or over-seer of all whatsoever was to be done in the house, and to have command over the slaves, and other two Damosells of *Leonora's* age; to the end that she might entertaine her selfe with those of her owne yeares, whom he had made choice of for that purpose.

He promised that he would treate and use them well, and that he would regular them all in such sort, giving them such good content, that they should not risent this their retyrednesse. And that on festivall dayes, they should without fayle goe to heare Masse; but that was so early in the morning, that the light could scarce come to see them.

His servants and slaves promised him that they would doe what-soever hee should be pleased to command them, without any the least repining, with a very prompt and willing minde. And the new married wife shrinking up her shoulders, and bowing downe her head, sayd; that she had no other will, save that of her Husband, and Lord, whereunto she would ever be obedient.

This prevention being made, and good *Carrizales* now fully setled in his owne house; he began to enjoy as well (poore man) as he could, the fruits of matrimonie.

Thus did she passe away the time with her Governesse, Damosells, and Slaves; and they, that they might passe it over the better, pampred up themselves with good cheere; and few dayes past over their heads, wherein they did not make a thousand *Quelc-choses,* whereunto their honey, and their Sugar which they had in most plentifull manner, gave a very daintie and delicate relish.

There was no lacke of any thing that was needfull, they had enough, and more then enough, and their master was willing that it should be so; opinionating with himselfe, that by this his liberall and large allowance, he should keep them entertained and occupied without having cause given them, whereby to call to minde, or so much as once thinke of this their close imprisonment.

Leonora, looke what her servants did, the same did shee; she had no other companie, and was therfore forced to entertain the time with such entertainments as they thought fittest. Nay such was her simplicitie, that she fell to making of babies, and other the like childish things, which shewed the plainesse and harmlessenesse of her disposition, and the tendernesse of her yeares. All which gave exceeding great satisfaction to her jealous husband; it seeming unto him, that he had hit right in chosing the best kinde of life that he could possibly devise, or imagine; and that by no manner of meanes, either humane industry, or mallice, could disturbe his quiet; and therefore did onely studie and beate his braines, to bring home rarities, and dainties to please and content his wife, entreating her that whatsoever she had a mind to, she would acquaint him with it, and she should have it whatsoever it cost him, holding nothing she desired to deare for her.

Those dayes wherein she went to Masse, (which was as hath beene sayd, betweene the two lights) her Parents came, and there in the Church talked with their Daughter, but still before her husband, that he might be an eare-witnesse of what they sayd; who gave them so many gifts, that although they did much pittie their Daughter, and inwardly grieve at that restraint wherein she lived; yet did they dissemble this their distaste, and bare their sorrow the more patiently, by reason of those many great gifts and favours which their liberall Son in Law *Carrizales* continually conferred on them.

He used to rise betimes in the morning, staying within till the *Dispensero* came, whom over night by a scroll or bill which he left in the Tornell, advised him what he should bring the next day. And as soone as the *Dispensero* was come, and dismissed; *Carrizales* instantly got him out of doores, and for the most part a foot, leaving those two doores towards the street shut, and that in the middle, and betweene both remained the *Negro.*

He went abroad about his businesses, which being few, were soone dispatcht, so that he quickly returned home againe; and shutting up himselfe, he retained himselfe in regalaring and making much of his wife, and in cheering up his servants, who lov'd him very well, and wisht him all happinesse; because his carriage was plaine, and pleasing; as also, for that towards all of them he was so liberall and bountifull. Thus had they now passed one whole yeare of their *Noviciation,* or *Probationorshippe,* and now made profession of that kinde of life; having resolved with themselves to continue therein till the end of his; and peradventure would have made good this their deter‑ mination, if that subtill and cunning perturber of humane peace had not hindred it, as by and by you shall heare.

Tell me now, he who takes himselfe to be the discreetest and wariest amongst men, what better or surer preventions could old *Carrizales* have used for to make all safe and secure, since that by no meanes he would not permit that within his house there should bee any one creature that was a Male: no, not so much as a Cat to persecute the Mice, nor a little dogge to lie in his wifes lappe to sport and play withall, all these were of the feminine gender, none of the masculine, save onely himselfe. In the day hee mused much, in the night he slept little; he was the watch and centinell of his house, and the *Argos,* who had still a vigilant eye over her whom he so dearely loved. Never did any man come within his doores, no not so much as into the outward Court. With his friends and acquaintance he did negociate and treate in the open street.

The figures in those his hangings which did adorne his Hall, and other his with drawing roomes, and chambers, were all Females, Flowers, Trees, and the like Boscage‑worke. All his whole house did smell of honesty, retyrednesse, and reservednesse; yea, even in those tales which in the long and tedious nights of winter his servants told by the fire side, to passe away the time; for that he was present, not in any one of them was uttered any the least kind of lascivious or wanton word.

The silver of the old mans hoary hayres, to the eyes of *Leonora* seemed to be of pure gold; because the first love which Virgins enjoy, leaves an impression in their soule, as a seale doth in waxe. His strict guard upon her, seemed to her to be advised circumspection; for she did think and beleeve, that what passed with her, the like passed with all those that were newly married. Her thoughts never went a gadding beyond the walls of her owne house; nor did her will desire any one thing, save what was her husbands pleasure. Onely those dayes which shee went to Masse, she saw the streetes; and this too was so earely, that unlesse it were in her returne homeward from Church, there was not light enough to behold them. Never was there seene any Monastery so close kept, never any *Nunnes* more retyred, nor those golden Apples of old so narrowly watcht; and yet notwithstanding all this, he could in no wise prevent nor avoyd the falling into that which he so much feared, at least in thinking it to be so.

There is a certaine kinde of idle people in *Sevill*, handsome proper yong men, well both borne, and clad; who in a braverie and gallantry, take great pride and glorie in courting women; seeking by all possible meanes to winne those beauties to their will, whereunto they stand affected. This they make their studie, and therein employ the utmost of their wits.

Now one of these gallants (a single man) had taken notice of this house of warie *Carrizales,* and finding it alwaies shut; hee had a great itching desire to know who lived there within; and using his best diligence, but with a great deale of caution, and cunning, hee came to a full knowledge of that which hee desired; informing himselfe of all the particular passages point by point. All which did but kindle a greater and more enflamed desire in him, to see if it were possible to winne by force, or industry; a fort so well and strongly guarded.

And acquainting two or three other of his friends of the same feather with the businesse, and of his purpose; they did encourage and

hearten him on, for to put it in execution; for in such kinde of actions, counsellours, and helpers are seildome wanting. The maine difficultie which offered it selfe unto them, was the manner that was to be held, for the attempting and undertaking of so hard and dangerous a peece of service. And having entered often into consultation, and sate in counsell what course were best to be taken, with a joynt consent, they agreed at last on this.

That *Loaysa* (for so was this young gallant called) feigning to goe out of Towne for some certaine time should remove himselfe from the sight of his friends and acquaintance, and so he did. This being done hee puts mee on a paire of drawers next to his bodie of very pure white linnen, and a cleane shirt of curious fine holland; but on the toppe of them, hee had such ragged and tattered cloathes, so patched, and so peeced, that the poorest beggar in the Cittie, had none so bad. He had cut away a prettie part of his beard, clapt over one of his eyes a blacke patch, bound up one of his legges very straight with swathes one upon another; and resting his bodie on two crutches, hee personated a poore lame cripple; and acted that part so well, that none that were truly so taken in their limbes, could come neere him.

In this disguise and posture, night by night hee prayed at *Carrizales* his doore, which hee found still shut. The *Negro* (whose name was *Luys*) remaining mewed up betweene the two doores; there *Loaysa* leaning his backe against it, tooke out a little Ghitterne out of a greasie case, the instrument being none of the cleanest, wanting besides some strings; and for that hee had some snatch of musicke, hee beganne to play some merrie and lively tunes, and to sing thereto certaine prettie songs, and choisest ditties that hee could, changing the tone of his voyce that hee might not bee knowne.

Things being thus ordered, he fell anone after to sing some pleasant wittie Ballads of *Moores,* and *Moorish* Women; and that with such an odde kinde of grace, and gesture, and varying of the voyce, that as many as past along that streete, made a stand to heare him; and all the while hee continued singing, your boyes and girles, and younger sort of people flocked about him, hemming him in on every side. And *Luys* the *Negro*, laying his eares as close as hee could betweene the two doores; was so mightily taken with this musicke, that hee would have opened the doore with a very good will, and did endeavour it (but all in vaine) that he might to his greater contentment more fully heare it; such, and so great is the inclination which your *Negro's* naturally have unto musicke. And when *Loaysa* was willing that they who heard him, should leave him; he left off his playing and singing, put up his Ghitterne, and betaking him to his crutches, went his way.

Foure or five times he had given musicke to the *Negro*, and onely for his sake did he give it; it seeming unto him, that the place where he was to begin to make a breach in in this building, must be by the *Negro*, nor did his thought therein deceive him; for comming one night as hee was wont to the doore, he began to fall a tuning of his Ghitterne, and perceived that the *Negro* was alreadie very attentive; and drawing neere to the hindge of the doore, in a low voyce he called unto him, saying; I prethee (good *Luys*) if it be possible give me a little water, for I am ready to perish for thirst; and am so drie, that I am not able to sing one note.

No, I cannot (replyed the *Negro*) though my life lay upon it; for I neither have the key to this doore, nor is there any the least hole or crannie whereby to give it thee.

Who then (sayd *Loaysa*) hath the key? My master (answered the *Negro*,) who is the most jealous man in the World. And if he should but know that there were any bodie now speaking here with me, it were as much as my life were worth, he would not let me live one houre longer. But who are you that beg this water of me?

I (replied *Loaysa*) am a poore cripple, lame on one of my legges, which is so benum'd, that I have no sence or use of it, getting my living by begging for Gods sake, an almes of good and well-disposed people. And besides (which is no small comfort and helpe for my better maintenance) I teach some *Moores,* and other poore people to play on the Ghitterne, and now at this present I have three slaves, all *Negro's,* some young, some elder; whom I have taught in such sort, that in any Taverne or other drinking schoole wheresoever they come, they can sing to any tune, and play any dance they call for, who have payd me very well for my paines.

I would pay you much better (sayd *Luys*) had I but the opportunitie to learne; but that is not possible, because my Master when he goes forth in the morning, shuts the doore to the street; and when he returnes he does the like, leaving me immured between two doores.

I sweare unto thee *Luys* (replied *Loaysa*) for he knew before hand the name of the *Negro,* if thou couldst but thinke upon, or devise any meanes how I might get in, in the night time, to teach thee to take out some lessons, I would in a fortnight make thee play so well on the Ghitterne, that thou shouldst not be ashamed to play at the corner of any street whatsoever in *Sevill*; for I would have thee to know, that I have an excellent gift in teaching. And moreover, (which will be a good helpe) I have heard that thou art very apt to learne, and of a nimble and quicke apprehension; and by that which I perceive already, if I have any judgement in me, that organ of thy voice tells mee, that it is a treble, and shouldest therefore sing wondrous cleare and well.

I have none of the worst voices I tell you, (answered the *Negro*) but what good does that doe me, since that I know no other tune, save that of *Estrella de Venus,* and that of *Por un verde prado,* and that which is now most in use; *A los hierros de una reia la turbada mano asida.*

All these are toyes (quoth *Loaysa*) and not worth a pin, in compari- son of those that I can and will teach thee. For I know all those of the

Moore Abiudarraez with those of his Ladie *Xarifa,* and all those which are sung touching the story of the *Grand Sophi Tomunibeyo,* together with those of the *Zarabanda,* so highly esteemed; which are such ravish‐ing tunes, that the *Portugueses* themselves are rapt therewith, and are for the time as it were in a trance. And these I teach with such dexteritie, and facilitie, that though thou shouldst be somewhat hard in apprehending them, and not beate thy braines much about them, thou shalt scarce have eaten three or foure bushells of salt; but thou shalt see thy selfe so improved, that thou shalt passe currant for one of the best players on the Ghitterne, of all the *Negro's* in this Countrey. Hearing him say so, the *Negro* sighed, and sayd; what booteth all this, since I know not how I shall get thee into the house?

We may (sayd *Laoysa*) finde a good remedy against that rubbe. Doe you but worke the meanes to get your Masters keyes, and I will give you a peece of soft waxe, wherein you shall take the print of them in such manner, that the wards may remaine imprinted in the waxe. And then out of the great affection which I have taken to thee, I will procure a cunning Locke‐smith, a friend of mine, to make the keyes accordingly; and so in the night I may come in unto thee, and teach thee to play better then *Prester Iohn* of the *Indies*; for it is a thousand pitties, that such a voice as thine should be lost, for want of being holpen by the Ghitterne. For I must tell thee (brother *Luys*) that the best voice in the World loseth of its qualities, when it is not accompanied with some instruments, be it either Ghitterne, Lute, Harpe, Organ, or the like. But that which will fit best with your voice, is that of the Ghitterne, for that it is the more handy, and lesse costly of all other instruments.

I am of your minde for that (replied the *Negro,*) but that which you propound can not be done, because the keyes never come to my hands, nor doth my Master let them goe out of his, day nor night, they sleepe with him underneath his pillow.

Then doe this other thing *Luys*, (sayd *Loaysa*) if thou haſt a minde to be a perfeƈt and compleate musitian; if not, I have done, and will not trouble my selfe any further in advising thee. Have a mind (answered *Luys*,) yes marry have I, and so great, that I would leave nothing undone, no ſtone unmoved, on that condition it were possible that by your meanes I might come to bee a good Musitian. Doubt you not of that, replyed *Loaysa*; I will give you therefore in at this doore, you making way for them, by removing some little quantity of ſtone, or earth neere the hinges; I will give thee I say, a paire of pinsars, and a hammer, wherewith thou mayſt in the dead of the night, plucke out the nayles of the locke with a great deale of faciⅼitie, and with no lesse easinesse, faſten them againe to the plate in such sort, that it shall not be perceived that it had beene unnayled and taken off. And I being shut up with you in your Hay-loft, or there where you lodge, and you shall see very shortly what I can doe, and sooner perhaps then I have sayd, or you can imagine; for the making good of my promise, the encreasing of mine owne credit, and your improvement. And for to have wherewithall to eate and suſtaine our selves; take you no care, for I will bring provision enough with me for both of us, which shall serve us for eight or nine daies; for I have schollers and friends (I thanke God) who will not see mee want any thing.

As for our dyet (replied the *Negro*) that is the leaſt thing we need to feare; for what with my Maſters allowance, and that which my fellow servants give me of that which is left, we shall have viƈtualls enough, and to spare, for two more besides our selves. Doe you bring the hammer and pinsars you speake off, and let me alone for to make way for the getting of them in, and for the damming up of the place againe, that it may not be perceived. And although I shall be driven to ſtrike some blowes with the hammer in taking off the plate; yet my Maſters bed-chamber where he sleepes, is so farre off from this doore, that it muſt be either a great miracle, or misfortune, if hee hap to heare us.

Well (sayd *Loaysa*) let us put that to the venture, and within these two dayes (*Luys*) thou shalt have all that is necessarie for the putting of this thy vertuous purpose in execution. And let mee advise you to refraine from such meates as breed fleagme; for besides that, in themselves they are not wholesome, they are very hurtfull for your voyce. No one thing (replied *Luys*) makes mee so much hoarse as wine, yet will I not be debarr'd my drinking of it, for all the voyces in the world.

No by no meanes (sayd *Loaysa*,) it was the least of my thought; God forbid that I should forbid you so good a thing. Drinke (my son *Luys*) drinke, and much good may it doe thy heart; for wine that is drunke with measure, doth never cause any harme. Nay I drinke it with measure I assure you (replied the *Negro*;) for I have a jarre, which being fill'd to the very brimme, holds just three quarts, and no more, nor no lesse. And this my fellow slaves bring me unwitting to my Master. And the *Dispensero* ever and anone, but very secretly, furnishes me with a bottle which holds just a gallon, for a new supply when my jarre begins to grow low. I tell thee (sayd *Loaysa*) just such a kinde of life doe I leade, and there is no living without it; for, *La seca garganta, ni giune ni canta,* A drie throat, cannot sing a note.

Well, fare you well (sayd the *Negro*;) but one word with you before you goe, see you doe not misse singing here night by night, till you bring those tooles with you to worke your enterance in hither, for my fingers ends itch to be fingering of the Ghitterne. Misse singing (said *Loaysa*) no, I will dye first; and to give you the more content when I come next, I will tickle your eares with other new tunes. Oh by all meanes (replied *Luys*) that will be excellent; New tunes? thou mak'st my heart leape for joy. But I pray thee doe not goe hence, before thou hast sung one song more, that I may sleepe the better after it; and for paying you for your paines, beleeve mee though I am but poore, I will pay you better then those that are richer. I doe not stand upon that (answered *Loaysa*) for according as you profit, so shall you pay me, and no otherwise. And now hearken to this tune, and I hope you will like it; but if it be my good hap once to get in to you, thou shalt see wonders; with a very good will (answered the *Negro*.) This large colloquie being ended, *Loaysa* sung a witty conceited dittie, wherewith the *Negro* was so well pleased, and satisfied, that hee thought every houre a thousand yeares, till he might see the doore opened.

Loaysa was scarce gone from the doore, when as with much more nimblenesse then his crutches promised, hee hastened to give an account to his companions and counsellers, of this his good beginning, as a prognosticke of the good end which hee hoped for. He met with them, finding them altogether, and recounted unto them what hee had concluded with the *Negro*. And the next day following, he fitted him with such instruments, as should pull out any nayle, or knap it asunder, as if it were some small sticke. But in the meane while, *Loaysa* was not carelesse in his comming to give the *Negro* musicke; nor was the *Negro* negligent in making a hole for the receiving of those tooles which his Master should bring him, and to cover it in such sort; that if it were not looked on with a malicious and suspicious eye, it could never be espied.

The second night *Loaysa* gave him those instruments, and *Luys* tried his strength, and in a manner without putting any force at all, hee found the nayles, some pulled out broken, and some whole, and the plate in his hands, he oppened the doore, and let in his *Orpheus*, and new master. But when he saw him with his two crutches, and so ragged and torne, and his legge so bound about with swathes, he was wonder strucken. *Loaysa* had not clapt his blacke patch upon his eye, because then it was not needfull; and thus accoutered, as soone as hee entered in, hee hugged his good scholler in his armes, and kissed his cheek, and presently put into his hands a great bottle of wine, and

a boxe of conserves, with some other sweet-meates which he had brought in a wallet along with him. And throwing his crutches away from him, as if hee had not any infirmitie at all, he began to cut two or three capers, whereat the *Negro* was much more amazed then before, admiring what manner of man this should bee, and to what end or purpose hee had put on this disguise. To whom (to put him out of his musing) *Loaysa* sayd;

Know (brother *Luys*) that this my lamenesse, and numbnesse, does not grow from any infirmitie that I have, but of set purpose, I feigne my selfe to bee thus ill affected whereby I get my living, and bread to put in my mouth, begging for Gods sake. And helping my selfe with this tricke, and my musicke, I picke out a pretty meanes to maintaine my selfe, and leade the merriest life of any man in the world; whereas they who are not their craft-masters, and use not the like kinde of industrie, are readie to starve, and often dye out of meere hunger. And this thou shalt finde to be true, as in the discourse of this our new-founded friendshippe I shall discover and make clear unto thee.

Time will shew it, answered the *Negro*; in the meane while let us take order to put this plate againe in its owne place, that what wee have done may not bee discerned. With a very good will, replyed *Loaysa*; and so taking nayles out of his wallet, they fastened the plate so neatly to the locke, that it was just the same as it was before; wherewith the *Negro* rested wonderfull well contented. And so *Loaysa* going up to the *Negro's* loft, accommodated himselfe the best hee could. *Luys* presently tinded a waxe candle, and without any longer tarrying, *Loaysa* drew out his Ghitterne, and playing upon it with a soft and sweete touch, suspended the *Negro* in such sort, that hearing it, hee was almost out of his little wits. Having played a pretty while, hee tooke out a new collation, and gave it unto his Scholler, who in swallowing downe his sweet meats, dranke so deepe of the bottle, that it made him more besides himselfe then the musicke.

This being past and ended, hee would in all haste, that *Luys* should beginne to take out his first lesson; and because the poore *Negro* had foure fingers thicke of wine swimming in his braine, hee could not hit right upon any one of the frets, or make any true stoppe; and yet notwithstanding *Loaysa* made him beleeve that he had learned alreadie two tunes, and the jeast was, that the good silly *Negro* did verily thinke so indeed. And all that night, hee did nothing else but fumble on a Ghitterne out of tune, and worse strung, wanting its most necessarie strings thereunto belonging.

That little of the night which was left them, they slept. And about sixe in the morning *Carrizales* came downe and opened the middle doore, and likewise that towards the streete, and stood wayting there for the *Dispensero,* who came anone after; and putting in the provision for the house at the *Tornell,* hee went thence and called to the *Negro* that hee should come quickly downe and take in the provender for the Mule, and with it his allowance for himselfe. Which hee had no sooner done, but old *Carrizales* went his way in great haste, leaving both doores lockt, not perceiving that which was done in that to-wards the streete; whereof the Master, and his Scholler were not a little glad thereat.

Scarce had the Master of the house got him out of doores, but hee hastily snatcht up the Ghitterne, and began to play so loud thereon, that all the Maydes in the house heard the sound thereof; and calling unto him, askt him at the *Tornell.* What is this *Luys*? whence had you this Ghitterne? who gave it you? Who gave it mee (answered *Luys*) the best Musitian living in the world, and one that hath faith-fully undertaken to teach me in lesse then sixe dayes, more then sixe thousand tunes. But where is this Musitian sayd the old beldame that was mother of the maydes? Not farre off, replied the *Negro*; and if it were not for shame, and the feare I have of my Master; peradventure I could shew him you with a wet finger, and I vow you would be very glad to see him. But where may he be, that we may see him, answered the beldame? since that into this house never entered any other man, save our owne Master. You say well Mistresse (sayd the *Negro*) but I will say nothing till you see that which I know, sure I am he hath taught me what I told you, in so short a space. Certainely (sayd the old Dame) if it be not the Devill that hath taught thee, I know not who can make thee turne so good a Musitian, in so short

88

a time. Go, get you gone (quoth the *Negro*) for one of these dayes, you shall both heare, and see him. That cannot bee, replied another of the maydes; for we have no windowes out towards the ſtreete, either to see, or heare any thing. Very good, quoth the *Negro*; but yet let me tell you, that there is a remedie for all things, save againſt death; and so much the rather, if you can, or know how to hold your peace. Hold our peace, (replied one of the slaves,) we will bee more silent, then if we were dumbe. I assure thee (brother *Luys*) that like one that hath a longing, I am readie to dye, to heare a good voice; for since that we have beene here mewed up like so many Hawkes, we have not so much as heard the singing of birds.

All this prattle *Loaysa* heard, to his passing great contentment, it seeming unto him, that they all tended to the perfecting of his pur⁄pose; and that good fortune had put to her helping hand, in cutting out the cloth according to the measure of his owne will. The Maydes went their way upon the *Negro's* promising them, that when they leaſt thought on it, hee would call them to heare a very good voice. And fearing leaſt his Maſter should returne, and finde him talking with them; he left them for the present, retyring himselfe to his lodging. Hee would feigne have beene tampering with a new lesson, but he durſt not touch the Ghitterne in the day time, leaſt his Maſter might chance to heare him, who came a little while after; and shutting the doores as he was wont, lockt himselfe up in his house.

When the *Negro* had his dinner given him that day at the *Tornell*, *Luys* sayd to the *Negro* that brought it him; that that night after that his Maſter was a bed and asleep, they should all come downe to the *Tornell*, and that without all fayle they should heare the voice he promised them. True it is, that before he told them this, hee had with moſt earneſt entreaties, besought his Maſter that he would be pleased to play and sing that night at the *Tornell*, that he might make good his word, and cumply with the promise hee had made, that the Maydes should heare an admirable voyce; assuring him, that he should be much made of by all of them.

His master after a great deale of entreating, yeelded at last to doe that which the *Negro,* or rather himselfe so much desired. Howbeit he made shew that it was onely at his schollers request, and to give him content, without any other interest of his owne. The *Negro* embraced him, and gave him a kisse on the cheek, in token of the contentment, which that his promised favour had caused in him; and that day he feasted *Loaysa,* and made him better cheere then peradventure he should have found at home.

The night came, and in the midst thereof, little more or lesse, they began to heare a whispering about the *Tornell;* whereby *Luys* presently understood, that the whole packe of them were gathered there together. And calling to his Master, they came both downe from the Hay-loft, with a well strung, but better tuned Ghitterne. *Luys* ask't who, and how many there were of them that were to heare him? They answered, they were all there save only their Mistris who was in bed with her husband; for the which *Loaysa* was very sorry; yet notwithstanding, hee was willing to give an induction to his designe, and to give satis-faction to his scholler; and so touching with a soft and gentle hand his Ghitterne, he did play so sweetly, that the *Negro* wondered thereat, and the women that heard him were ravished therewith. What shall I say? they thought when they heard him play *loth to depart,* and that taking tune of the *Zarabanda,* the newest then in *Spaine.* There was not the oldest amongst them which did not fall a dancing; nor the yongest which did not tricke it with their armes a kembo; but very softly, and with a strange kind of silence, having set Sentinels, and spyes, to give them notice, if the old man should chance to wake.

Loaysa likewise sung a merry pleasant Ballad, wherewith he sealed up the eares of his *Auditors,* who earnestly intreated the *Negro,* that hee would tell them, who was this so rare a Musitian? The *Negro* told them, That he was a poore beggar, but withall, the gallantest, and bravest gentleman, of all that beggerly Corporation in *Sevill.* They then intreated him, that he would so order the businesse, that they might come to have a sight of him, and that for a fortnight he should not let him goe out of the house, and that they would entertaine him all that while very well, and that he should lack nothing, that was needfull for him. Then they asked him, how he came to get him into the house? Hereunto, hee returned them not one word; but told them, that if they had a mind to see him, they should make a little hole in the *Tornell,* which afterward they might stop up with Waxe; and that he would take it upon him, to keepe him in the house.

Loaysa spake likewise unto them, offering them his service, in such good language, that thereby they did perceive, that such words could not come from the wit of a poore beggar. They intreated him, that he would repayre another night to the same place, and that they would procure their Mistris to come downe to heare him, maugre the light sleepe of their Master, which lightnesse grew not from his many yeares, but from those many jealousies that he had in his head.

Whereunto *Loaysa* answered, that if hee would heare him without fearing the old mans troubling them, hee would give them a powder to put into his wine, that should make him sleepe soundly above his ordinarie time. God blesse me sayd one of the Damosels, if this prove true, what good fortune hath entered within our doores, without our dreaming, or deserving it. This will not bee so much a powder of sleepe for him, as a powder of life for all of us; and more particularly for our poore Mistris *Leonora,* his wife, who is never from her, *ni a sol, ni a sombra,* neither night, nor day, not suffering her to bee out of his sight one sole minute. Oh sweet sir, if ever you will doe any thing for us, and that our best wishes may wait on you in all that you desire or endeavour; bring this powder, delay no time, bring it, bring it I beseech you, and it shall be my taske to mixe it with his wine, I will be his skinker; and I wish it with all my heart that the old ladde may sleep three whole dayes, and so many nights, that we may have as many of mirth and jollitie.

Doubt ye not but I will bring it, sayd *Loaysa,* and such a one shall it be, that it shall do him no other hurt that takes it, save to provoke him to a most profound sleepe. Then all of them joyntly besought him, that he would bring it as soone as possibly hee could. And so resolving the next night to bore a hole with an augour in the *Tornell,* and to draw their Mistris thither, that she might see, and heare him, they tooke their leaves.

And the *Negro,* though it were neere upon breake of day, would needes take forth a new lesson which *Loaysa* gave him; and withall made him beleeve, that of all the schollers that ever he taught, not any one had a better eare then himselfe; yet the poore *Negro* knew not, nor ever would come to know what a musicall note meant.

Loaysa his friends tooke it to their care, to come nightly to listen between the two doores of the streete, to see if their friend had any thing to say unto them, or if hee needed ought; and making a certain signe, agreed upon between themselves; *Loaysa* knew that they were at the doore, and at the hole before mentioned. He gave them a short account of the good tearmes whereon his businesse stood; earnestly entreating them, that they would seeke out something that would procure sleepe, for to bee given to *Carrizales.* For he had heard some say, that there were some powders which would worke this effect. They told him that they had a Phisitian a friend, that would give them the best that he knew, or had, for that purpose. And so animating him to prosecute the enterprize hee had undertaken, and promising him to bring it him the next ensuing night, they speedily tooke their leave.

Night came, and the whole flocke of Pigeons came at the call of the Ghitterne; together with them, came that simple soule *Leonora,* fearefull and trembling least her husband should awake; for though she, overcome with this feare, was not willing to come; yet so many perswasions did her servants use, and more especially her Governesse spake so much in the praise of the sweetnesse of the musick, and the good disposition of the Musitian, that although she had never seene him, yet shee lifted him up above the clouds, and preferred him before *Absalom,* and *Orpheus.* So that the poore Gentlewoman, convinced, and overswayed by them, yeelded to do that which she had no will to do, nor ever would have had.

The first thing they did, was to bore a hole in the *Tornell* for to see the Musitian, who was not now in the habit of a poore mendicant, but in a suite of coloured Taffata, bedawbed all over with gold lace, and a hat answerable therunto, with exceeding neate linnen in his band and cuffes wherewith hee came provided in his wallet; imagining that hee might happily meete with some such good occasion wherein it might be fitting for him to change his habite. He was young, of a gentle disposition, and a good presence. And (because he had so much time to friend, that all of them had taken a full view of him,) comparing him with their old Master; he seemed unto them to be an Angell, one peeped through the augar-hole to see him, and then another; and in conclusion all, one after another. And to the end that they might view him the better, the *Negro* waving his wax candle, one while this way, another while that way, from side to side, from top to toe, gave them a full and perfect sight of his person.

Now when as they had made an end of feeding their eyes, and left further looking on him; *Loaysa* betooke him to his Ghitterne, and sung that night so farre beyond those other heretofore, that he strucke them all, old, and young with a strange astonishment. And all of them besought *Luys,* that he would invent some meanes how to bring in his Master amongst them, that they might heare, and see him neerer hand, and not at that distance, and through so narrow a hole; as likewise that they may bee rid of their feare by being so far off from their Master, who might suddenly come stealing in upon them and take them napping; which could not so succeed, if they tooke him into the house, and hid him closely amongst them.

But this course was crost by their Mistris, who mainely withstood it, and would by no meanes give way to his admittance amongst them, saying; Content your selves, can we not as well see and heare him here; sure I am we may doe both with more safetie, and lesse hazzard of our honour. What doe you talke of honour? sayd her Governesse, the King hath enough for us all; goe I pray and shut up your selfe with your *Methusalem,* and leave us to make merrie and enjoy our selves as we may. And the rather may we give him free entrance, for that he seemes to be so honest a gentleman, that hee will no other thing of us, then what we will our selves.

Hence *Loaysa* taking his rise, sayd; Gentlewomen, I am come hither with no other intention, save onely to serve you with my soule, and my life; condoling with you this your unheard of, and never untill now seene the like close shutting up, pittying the time which in this strickt kinde of life ye lose. I am a man (I sweare unto you by the life of my Parents) so milde, so meeke, so plaine in my dealing, of so good a condition, and so obedient, that I shall never do any thing more then what you shall command me. And if any, even the meanest amongst you shall but say unto mee, Master sit downe here and stirre not, master passe to this, or that other place of the house, keepe you close in such a corner, lye downe and wagge not, I will doe as you bid me, and with more nimblenesse and celeritie, then the tamest dog that is taught to leape and dance for the King of *France.*

If he will doe as he sayes (sayd the as ignorant as innocent *Leonora*) what meanes may wee use that this our musicall Master may have accesse unto us? Very good meanes, replied *Loaysa*; doe you but get the print of this middle-doore-key in wax, and against to morrow night, I will get another made like unto it, which shall serve our turne. In taking this one key out in waxe, we take out all the rest to the whole house; because this is the master-key that opens and commands all, answered one of the Damosells. So much the better (sayd *Loaysa*;) You say true sayd *Leonora*. But sir you shall first sweare, that you shall not doe any other thing when you are entered in, save onely sing, and play when you shall bee commanded; and that you shall submit your selfe to bee shut up, and to rest there quiet where we shall put you, till we release you. I sweare to keepe all this truely, answered *Loaysa*. Nay, this oath is nothing worth (replied *Leonora*;) you shall sweare (sayd she) by the life of your father, and by the life of your mother. I sweare (said *Loaysa*) by the life of my father, and by the life of my mother. This done, another of the damosells sayd unto him; see (sir) that you doe not forget the powder, for that is *tu autem* of all.

With this, ceased the conversation of that night, all resting wondrous well contented with the consentment which they had made amongst themselves. And fortune, who from good to better, went furthering *Loaysa's* affaires, who brought his friends to that streete two houres after mid-night; who making their wonted signe, playing on a Iewes-trumpe. *Loaysa* spake unto them, telling them how things stood with him, and how farre hee had proceeded in his pretension; entreating them that they would bring him the powder, or some other thing which hee had formerly spoken for, for to cast *Carrizales* into a sound and deepe sleepe. Hee acquainted them likewise with that of the master key; they told him, that either the powder, or an oyntment should bee brought him the night following, being of such force and vertue; that the pulses and temples being anoynted therewith, would cause a most heavie sleepe, out of which there was no awaking of a man in two dayes, save by washing with vinegar all those parts which had beene annoynted; and that if hee would give them the key in waxe, it should be made out of hand.

This short dialogue being ended, they with-drew themselves; and *Loaysa,* and his scholler slept that little part of the night which remained. *Loaysa* expecting with great longing that which was to come, to see if they would cumply with their word concerning the promised key. And tho time seeme slow and lazie to those that waite upon it, yet at last it goes along with our thought, and comes to meete in that point as we would have it, because it never stands still, but is still going on.

Well, the expected night was now come, and the accustomed houre of repayring to the *Tornell,* whether came all the servants of the house, great, and small, blacke, and white, for all of them were desirous to see this our Musitian within their *Seraglio,* but *Leonora* came not. And *Loaysa* asking for her, answere was made, that she was in bed with her Husband, who had locked the doore of his lodging; and after that hee had thus shut it, when he had layd himselfe down to sleepe, he clapt the key underneath his pillow, and that their Mistris had told them, that when the old man was fallen fast asleepe, shee would take from under him the masters key, and imprint the same in waxe; and that for that purpose shee had alreadie prepared it, and made it soft for impression; and that within a little while after, they should come and fetch it at the out side of the hole, which was made of purpose in the doore, for a Doe-Cat to come in at. *Loaysa* wondered much at the warinesse of the old man, yet for all this their desire was not daunted.

Now whilest they were talking of this subject, hee heard the Iewes-trumpe; hee hastened to them at that call, and found that they were his friends, who gave him a little boxe of oyntment, having that property before specified. *Loaysa* tooke it, and wished them to stay a while, and hee would bring them a patterne of the key. Hee returned backe againe to the *Tornell,* and told *Leonora's* Governesse, who was shee that with most earnestnesse desired his enterance of the boxe;

and that shee should carry it forthwith to her Mistris, acquainting her with the propertie it had; and that shee should annoynt her husband so gently with it, that hee might not perceive it, and shee should see it worke wonders. The Governesse did so, and comming to the Cats

hole, shee found that *Leonora* was expecting her, lying all along on the ground, with her face towardes the hole; whether her Governesse being come, she stretched her selfe out at length after the same manner, and clapping her mouth to her Mistris eare, and speaking in a low voyce, told her, she brought the oyntment, and after what manner she was to make tryall of its vertue. She tooke the oyntment, and told her Governesse that by no meanes shee could come by her husbands keye, for hee had not put it under his pillow as hee was wont, but betweene the two *Cholcon's,* and in a manner under the very midst of

O

his body; but would have her tell the Master of musicke, that if the oyntment should worke that effect as hee sayd it would, then very easily could she take the key from under him as oft as she pleased; and therefore it would be needlesse to take it in waxe. Shee willed her to goe instantly and tell him so, and that she should returne backe againe to see how the oyntment wrought, for presently shee would anoynt him therwith. The governesse went down and did her Mistris message to *Loaysa,* and thereupon he dismissed his friends, who stood wayting for the key.

Trembling and quaking very softly, and not daring to draw her breath; *Leonora* went gently annoynting the pulses of her jealous hus- band, and likewise annoynted the windowes of his nosthrills, and when she came to them, it seemed unto her that he did startle at it, and was almost dead for feare, that shee should bee taken with the theft in her hand. In conclusion, in the best manner she could, she made an end of annoynting all those places which they had told her were needfull; which was all one as to have embalmed him for his buriall.

It was not long ere the oyntment had given manifest signes of its vertue; for anone after the old man began to snore so loud, that the musicke thereof might bee heard without in the streete, which was sweeter in her eares, then that of the Master in those of the *Negro.* And yet as one not fully secured by that which shee saw, and heard; she drew unto him, she jogg'd him first a little, and then a little more to see if hee would awake; and grew at last to be so bold, that she turn'd him from the one side to the other, without waking him.

When she saw this, she went to the hole in the doore, and with a voice, not so low as before, she called to her governesse, who was there wayting, and sayd unto her; give me *albricias,* some reward for my good newes. *Carrizales* sleepes as soundly, as if he were dead. Why then (Mistris) doe not you take the key from under him? sayd the governesse, the Musitian hath beene wayting for it this houre, and more. Stay a little (replied *Leonora*) I am now going for it; and turning up the bed, shee thrust her hand betweene the two *Colchon's*, and tooke out the key from out the midst of them, without the old mans feeling it. And holding it in her hand she began to leape for joy, and without any more adoe, she opened the doore and presented it to the governesse, who received it with the greatest gladnesse and contentment in the world.

Leonora commanded they should open to the Musitian, and being let in they should carry him to the gallery, not daring to bee farre from thence for feare of what might happen; and that in any case they should take a new oath of him, that he should not doe ought save what they appointed him, and that if he should not ratifie and confirme it anew, in no manner of wise should they open the doore unto him. It shall bee done (sayd the Governesse,) and I vow unto you that hee shall not enter till that he hath sworne, and sworne againe. Doe not limit him (sayd *Leonora*;) but more especially be you sure that he sweare by the life of his father, and his Mother, and by that which hee loves best, for so shall wee rest secure, and wee shall have our fill of hearing him sing, and play; and as I live he doth both very delicately. Be gone therefore, without delaying the businesse any longer, least we passe away the night onely in talking.

The good Governesse tucked up her cloathes, set her best foot forward, and in a trice came to the *Tornell* where all the people of the house stood expecting her. And having shewed them the key which she brought along with her, so great was the contentment they all tooke, that they lifted her up above ground in their armes, crying, *vivat, vivat,* long live our governesse. And much more were they joyed, when shee told them that there was no neede of counterfeiting the key; for according to the rate of the sleeping of the anoynted old man, they might have the key as oft as they would. Good, very good sayd one of the Damosells; open this doore I pray, and let this gentleman in, that we may once see him. Be not so hasty (replied the governesse) there is more in it then to see him, for we must take an oath of him, as we did the other night. He is so good, and so honest (said one of the slaves) that he will not sticke upon oathes. Hereupon the governesse opened the doore, and keeping it halfe open, and halfe shut, she called to *Loaysa,* who had heard every word they sayd through the hole of the *Tornell*; who comming to the doore, would have entred all at once, but the governesse stopping him by putting her hand against his breast, sayd unto him.

Sir, I would have you to know, that all they who are within the doores of this house, are as true Virgins, as when their Mothers brought them forth, except my Mistris. And howbeit I may seeme unto you to bee forty yeares of age, having not as yet seen thirty, for I want two moneths and a halfe of it. And though happily I looke somewhat old, I may thanke the many troubles and crosses which have followed me; and those you know will adde one figure more, if not two to our yeares, according as they have beene more, or lesse. And this being so as it is, it stands not with reason, that in exchange of hearing two, three, or foure songs, we should put our selves to the hazard of losing so much Virginitie, as is here shut up within these walls; for even this *Negra*, whose name is *Guiomar,* is a virgine. And therefore sir, though my heart stands well affected towards you; before you enter here into our kingdome, you must take a solemne oath, that you shall doe nothing, save what we shall ordaine. And if it seeme unto thee, that much is that which wee require; consider that much more is that which we adventure. And if in comming hither your intention be good, you need not to be so nice and scrupulous in swearing. *Que albuen pagador, no le duelen prendas.* For he that is a good paymaster, will never be loth to lay downe a pawne.

Well, exceeding well hath our Miſtris *Marialonso* spoken, ſayd one of the Damoſells; and like a diſcreet woman, as well in this, as all other her actions; and therefore Miſtris if he will not ſweare, let him not him come in. Hereupon ſayd *Guiomar* the *Negra,* who could ſpeake a little broken *Spanish*; for my part ſweare, or ſweare not, be he what

he will be, let him come in; for though he ſweare never ſo much, when he is once in, he will forget all his oathes.

    Loaysa, with a great deale of patience and temper, hearkened to *Marialonso* her long *Harvenga*; and with a grave repoſedneſſe, returned this anſwere. Certainely, (my much honoured and reſpected friends) my intention never was, is, or ſhall be other, ſave to give you liking and content, as farre as my poore abilities can reach; and therefore ſhall not with an ill will take this oath you require of me, yet would I rather that you would have truſted me on my bare word; ſince that being given by ſuch a one as I am, it ſhould have beene as good, and as warrantable as any bond, or obligation whatsoever. I would have you to know that under a coarse cassocke, may be a Sattin suite; and that a thred-bare cloake, may cover a good drinker. But that all of you may rest secure of my good desire, I am resolved to sweare like an honest man. And therefore I sweare by all that, which in its *Proeame* the true history of *Charlemaine* containeth, together with the death of Gyant *Fierabras,* not to transgresse, nor goe beyond the bounds of the oath that I have taken, nor to swerve from the command of the least and meanest of these Virgins; upon paine that if I shall either in act, or in my desire doe otherwise, from this present, till then, and from then till now, I give it for voide, and of no effect and validitie.

So farre went *Loaysa* on with his oath, when as one of the Damosells, who with attention had given eare unto him, spake out aloud, saying; this is an oath to move the hardest stones to tender pittie; ill fortune befall me, if I suffer you to sweare any farther, for with that which you have alreadie sworne, you may enter into the signe of *Capricorne.* And taking hold of his breeches, she pull'd him in, and presently all the rest came flocking round about him; and one of them went instantly to advertise their Mistris thereof, who stood centinell, observing her husbands sleeping. And when the messenger told her that the Musitian was come into the gallery, shee was at one and the same instant both joyfull, and sad, and demanded if he had taken his oath? She answered, yes; and in such a new forme, as never in all her life shee had heard the like. Well (sayd *Leonora*) if he hath sworne, we have bound him fast enough. Oh how advisedly was it done of me, to put him to his oath.

In this interim, came up all the whole troope, and the Musitian in the midst of them; the *Negro Luys,* and the *Negra Guiomar,* lighting them up the stairs. And *Loaysa* no sooner saw *Leonora,* but hee made speedily towards her, making shew to throw himselfe at her feete, and tender his service unto her. She continued silent, and by signes willed him to rise; and al of them were as it were mute, without daring to speak a word, fearing least their Master should heare them; which being taken notice of by *Loaysa*, he told them; that they might boldly speake aloud, because the oyntment wherewith their Master was anoynted, had that force and vertue, that saving the taking away of life, it made a man for the time, as dead as a doore-nayle.

I beleeve it sayd *Leonora*, for if it were not so, hee had awaked twenty times ere this; since that his many indispositions, cause in him short sleeps, but since that I anoynted him, he snores like a horse. Seeing it is so (sayd *Marialonso*) let us goe to that hall which is right over against us, where we may heare him sing, and recreate our selves a little. Be it so sayd *Leonora*; but let *Guiomar* stay here and watch that she may advise us, if *Carrizales* should chance to awake. Whereunto *Guiomar* answered; the blacke must stay, whilest the white must play. The *Negra* stayd behinde, the rest went to the hall, where there was a rich *Estrado,* covered with *Turkie* Carpets, and costly Cushions whereon to sit; and placing the Musitian in the midst in a Chaire of Crimson velvet, they tooke their places and sate downe.

And *Marialonso,* mother of the maydes, taking a light in her hand, shee began to take a view of *Loaysa* from the crowne of the head, to the sole of the foot. Then sayd one of them; oh what a fine foretoppe, how well coloured, and how stiffe it is! Oh sayd another, what a sett of white teeth hee hath! what a bad yeare will this bee for blanched Almonds? for his teeth are more cleane and white then they. Then another; oh what a full and cleare eye hee hath! I sweare by the life of my mother, that they are like sparkling Diamonds. This, commended his mouth, comparing his lippes to Rubies; shee his legge and foote. And all of them together dissected the severall parts of his bodie, as if they had meant to make an Anatomie of him. Onely *Leonora* shee was silent, but tooke a fuller view of him then any of the rest, fixing her eyes steadily on him; and the more shee lookt on him, the more did hee seeme unto her to bee of a better presence then her aged Husband.

Whilest these things went taking up their contemplations, *Marialonso* tooke the Ghitterne which the *Negro* held, and put it into *Loaysa's* hands, entreating him that hee would play thereon, and that shee would sing a song which was then in great request, and mightily applauded in *Sevill*. The burthen of the song which shee sung was; *Mother, keepe me not under locke and key. Loaysa* cumplyed with her desire. They all of them rose up, and began to prepare themselves to dance. *Marialonso* had the whole ditty by heart, and sung the same with a better will, then voyce. The Verses were these.

> *Mother,*
>
> *Keepe me not under locke and kay,*
> *For who can hold what will away?*
> *If I doe not my selfe containe,*
> > *Your watch and ward is all in vaine.*
>
> *Set thou never so many spyes,*
> *Ore looking me with Argos eyes;*
> *Yet wil I finde time and leisure,*
> > *For to worke my wil and pleasure.*
>
> *Keepe me not under locke and kay,*
> *For who can hold what will away?*
> *If I doe not my selfe containe,*
> > *Your watch and ward is all in vaine.*
>
> *If that mine owne wel setled wil,*
> *Shal not shield me from what is ill;*
> *It is not feare, nor yet reward,*
> > *That cann womans honour guard.*

Keepe me not under locke and kay,
For who can hold what will away?
If I doe not my selfe containe,
    Your watch and ward is all in vaine.

Things forbidden we most desire,
Your flames supprest, augment the fire;
Rivers restrain'd, doe higher rise,
    So much doth Nature *freedome prize.*

Keepe me not under locke and kay,
For who can hold what wil away?
If I doe not my selfe containe,
    Your watch and ward is al in vaine.

The God of Love, wil finde a tricke,
Spight of your teeth, your locke to picke;
Love nere could yet restrained be,
    Whose nature 'tis for to live free.

Keepe me not under locke and kay,
For who can hold what wil away?
If I doe not my selfe containe,
    Your watch and ward is al in vaine.

Like to a bodkin in a bagge,
Like to a horne in a Stagge,
Or like to blushing in the face,
    Love to get out, wil finde a place.

Keepe me not under locke and kay,
For who can hold what will away?
If I doe not my selfe containe,
    Your watch and ward is all in vaine.

P

Danae shut up in a Tower,
Cupid *to show his mighty power,*
Caus'd Iove *in a golden shower,*
  To come and crop her Virgine flower.

Keepe me not under locke and kay,
For who can hold what will away?
If I doe not my selfe containe,
  Your watch and ward is al in vaine.

The Ayre *imprisoned in the earth,*
Rips up it's wombe to force it's birth;
Thunder teares the clouds, disdaining
  Ought should offer it's restraining.

Keepe me not under locke and kay,
For who can hold what will away?
If I doe not my selfe containe,
  Your watch and ward is all in vaine.

A full vessell that hath not vent,
Breakes hoope, and rests all torne and rent;
Then strive thou not Nature *to force,*
  For 'twill returne and have it's course.

Keepe me not under locke and kay,
For who can hold what will away?
If I doe not my selfe containe,
  Your watch and ward is all in vaine.

Wherefore (Mother) let me be free,
And live at mine owne libertie;
Since there is not that locke and kay,
  Which can hold fast what will away.

Keepe me not under locke and kay,
For who can hold what will away?
If I doe not my selfe containe,
Your watch and ward is all in vaine

The song being ended, and with it their dancing, wherin the Governesse *Marialonso* was their leader; they had scarse un-handed themselves, when loe, *Guiomar* their centinell came running in mightily troubled, quaking hand and foot, as if she had a shaking palsey; and with a hollow and low voice, sayd; my Master is awake Mistris, Mistris, my Master is awake; hye you hence, for he is up and comming hitherward. He, who hath seene a flocke of Doves feeding in the field, eating without feare what other mens hands have sowen; when at the cracking report of a discharged Peece, are affrighted, and rise and forgetfull of their food, astonished and amazed, betake them to their wings, cleaving therewith the ayre. Iust so let him imagine remained this flocke, and company of Dancers, frighted and amazed with the unexpected newes which *Guiomar* had brought them; and every one severally studying their excuse, and all of them joyntly seeking after their safety; one ranne to one place, another to another for to hide themselves in the roofes and corners of the house, leaving the Musitian all alone; who leaving his Ghitterne, and his singing full of perturbation, knew not in the world what to doe, or how to dispose of himselfe.

Leonora she wrung her faire hands, buffeted the face, tho but softly, of her Governesse *Marialonso*. In a word, all was confusion, amazement, and feare. But the governesse as one more subtill, and had her wits better about her then the rest; so ordered the businesse, that *Loaysa* should be put into her lodging chamber, and that her selfe, and her Mistris should abide still in the hall, and that an excuse should not be wanting to bee given to her old Master, in case he should come and finde them there.

Loaysa made presently the best shift he could to hide himselfe; and the governesse she was very attentive in listning whether her Master were comming, or no; and not hearing any the least noyse, she began to take heart, and by little and little, step after step, shee went drawing neerer and neerer to the chamber where her Master lodged, and heard that he snored as he did before. And being assured that he was asleepe, she tuck't up her clothes before, and re-turned running, craving *albricias* of her Mistris, of her Masters being asleepe, whom she willingly re-warded.

The good governesse would not lose that faire opportunitie, which of-fered it selfe unto her, of being the first enjoyer of those good parts which she imagined the Musitian had. And therefore telling *Leonora* that she should stay awhile in the hall, till shee went to call him; shee left her and went where hee was no lesse amazed, then pensive expecting the newes of what was become of the anointed old man, and what he did. He cursed the falsenesse of the oyntment, and complained of the credulitie of his friends, and accused his owne indiscretion, that he had not first made tryall thereof upon some other, before his experimenting of it upon *Carrizales*.

Whilest he was thinking on these things, in comes the Governesse, and assured him that the old man slept more, and better then he did before. His heart was much quieted herewith, and was very attentive to many amorous words which *Marialonso* uttered unto him, whereby hee collected her evill intention; and determined with himselfe, to make her the hooke and line wherewithall to fish her Mistris.

Now whilest these two were talking together, the rest of the servants who had hid themselves in divers parts of the house; one bolted out here, and another there, to see if it were true that their Master was awake. And perceiving that all was buried in deepe silence, they came to the Hall where they had left their Mistris, of whom they understood their Masters continuing still asleepe. And asking for the Musitian, and the Governesse, she told them where they were; and all of them with the selfe same silence and stilnesse which they brought with them, went faire and softly, hearkening at the doore what they two treated of.

The *Negra Guiomar* was not missing at this their parley, but the *Negro Luys* was wanting, for he no sooner heard that his Master was awake; but taking his Ghitterne along with him, he hastned to hide himselfe in his Hay-loft, and covering himselfe over head and eares with his poore bed-blanket; he sweated, and did so sweat for feare, one drop overtaking another, that his shirt was dung-wet. And yet for all this, hee did not forbeare tampering on the Ghitterne, which hee hugged close in his bosome, wronging the strings with his untunable fingering; such and so great (now fie upon him) was the affection which hee bare to Musicke.

The wenches over-heard the courtings and love trickes of the old Beldame, every one of them sent their bad wishes after her, some in one ill favoured phrase, and some in another; and not any one of them did call her old, but with an addition of Hagge, Witch, Bawde, and some other worse (if worse could bee) which for good respects I silence.

But that which moved most laughter in those that heard them, were the words which *Guiomar* the *Negra* uttered; who for that she was a *Portuguesse,* spake no good *Spanish,* yet very unhappily, and in a strange kinde of witty manner did play upon her, taxing her loose and wanton carriage. In effect, the conclusion of the discourse be-tween these two, was; that he would condiscend to her will, on con-dition, that shee should first deliver up her Mistris to his will. She offered to effect what he desired; so that in requitall thereof, he would cumply with her desire; for he had alreadie taken such full possession of her soule, that she cared not what impossibilities she promised, in an imaginary hope of procuring her own lustfull pleasure.

On these tearmes she left him, and went forth to speake with her Mistris; and seeing at her first stepping out that all the servants were got together about her doore, shee commanded them that they should with-draw themselves to their severall lodgings, and that the next night they should have time enough to enjoy both their wishes, and the Musitian with lesse disturbance, since that this night the feare they were put into, had much abated the edge, and sowred the sweet-nesse of their sport and jollitie.

All of them understood on what foot the old trot halted, and this was but a shift to rid them thence, that shee might be left alone by her selfe; yet durst do no otherwise but obey her, because she was mother of the maydes, and had the rule and command of them.

The maydes they were gone; the coast being now cleare, shee came into the hall to perswade her Mistris to yeeld unto *Loaysa's* will; and that in such patheticall manner in a long continued speech, and in such a smooth and well ordred a style, as if she had studied it many dayes before. She indeared unto her his gentile carriages, the sweetnes of his disposition, the vigour of his youth, his valour, his wit, and his many other graces and good parts. Furthermore painting forth unto her, how much more sweete and pleasing would the embracements of a young lover be, then those of an old decrepit husband; assuring her of all secresie and duration of delight, with divers other such like things as these, which the Devill had put into her tongue; shadowed over with rhetorical colours, and what varnish eloquence could lay upon them; so demonstrative and so effectuall, as might have moved not onely the tender heart of simple and unwary *Leonora*, but even that of the hardest marble. Oh ye smooth filed tongues! Oh ye pleyted vayles! the honourable weare of grave Matrons, chosen out of purpose for to authorize the roomes, and the *Estrados* of your principall Ladies; how contrary to your place and dutie, do ye exercise this your power-full, nay rather in a manner enforcing office!

Marialonso tooke her Mistris by the hand, and as it were by force (her eyes being full of teares) brought her thither where *Loaysa* was; and shutting the doore after her, shee left them there together, but went her selfe and layd her downe upon the *Estrado,* to see if she could take a little sleep, but for that shee had watched two nights before, over-come with drowsinesse, she fell fast asleepe on the *Estrado.*

Now, if at such a time and season as this a man should have asked *Carrizales,* had he not beene asleepe, what is become now of your well advised circumspections? your feareful jealousies? your wise animad-versions? your pithie perswasions? your wise and grave admonitions? What of those high wals of your house? what of there not entring thereinto any thing that should have the name, no not the shadow of a man? what of your close kept *Tornell?* your master-key? and your window without light? and that your strange and unheard of shutting up of all your people under locke and key? What of that great Dowrie wherewith you endowed *Leonora?* Those *Regalos,* and dainties, wherewith you continually entertained her? the good usage and liberall allowance of your servants, and slaves? and your not fayling in any one title in all that which you imagined they could possibly wish, or desire? But wee have told you alreadie, that there was no asking of him these and such other like questions; because hee slept somewhat a longer time then was needfull and expedient for him.

But admit hee should have heard all this, and put case hee should have made answere thereunto; hee could not have given a better, then in shrinking up his shoulders, in knitting of the browe, and in saying; All this building, the subtilitie of a wanton and vicious young man, the wickednesse of a false and Devillish Governesse, meeting with the unadvisednesse of an over-entreated, and perswaded young Woman, hath utterly demolished, and in an instant throwne downe to the ground.

But yet notwithstanding all this, the vertue and goodnesse of *Leonora* was such, that in that time which was most needfull for her, shee shewed her valour against those villanous enforcements, and base strivings of this cunning Impostor; and that with such strong and powerfull a resistance, that hee was not able to overcome her, but wearied himselfe in vaine, so that shee went away with the victory; and both of them being quite tyred out, and having over watcht themselves, fell fast asleepe.

Now when all was thus hush and quiet, Heaven had so ordered it; that *Carrizales* in despight of the oyntment, awaked; and (as his usuall custome and manner was) hee stretcht out his armes, and with his hands went feeling the bed from side to side, and not finding therein his beloved Wife; hee leapt out of the bed all amazed and astonished, with much greater nimblenesse then his many yeares promised; and when hee found her not in the Chamber, and saw the doore open, and that the key was wanting betweene the Colchones, hee was readie to runne out of his wits. But recollecting himselfe a little better, hee went out into the Gallerie, and going thence as soft as foot could fall, that hee might not bee heard, hee came into the Hall where the Governesse was sleeping; and seeing her all alone without *Leonora*, hee made to the lodging of the Governesse, and opening the doore very softly, hee saw that which hee could have wisht hee might never have seene; hee saw that which hee would have held a great happines that hee had no eyes for to see it. Hee saw *Leonora* in the armes of *Loaysa,* sleeping so soundly, as if the oyntment had wrought upon them, and not on the jealous old man.

Carrizales had quite lost the beating of his pulses, with the unex-pected sight of what hee saw, his voyce cleaved to his throat, his armes fell downe through faintnesse, so that hee stood still like a *Statua* of cold Marble. And though choller did its naturall office, seeking to

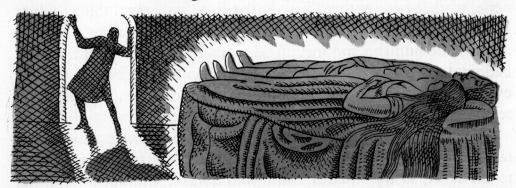

quicken and revive those his almost dead spirits; yet sorrow did so over-sway his anger, that it would scarce give him leave to fetch his breath. And yet notwithstanding, would hee have taken such revenge, as so great a wickednesse deserved; if hee had any weapon about him wherewith to have avenged himselfe of the wrong that was done him. And therefore resolved with himselfe to returne backe againe to his chamber to fetch a dagger; and at his returne, to take out the staines of his honour, with the bloud of these his two enemies, and together with theirs, that of all that infamous rabble of his house.

Having put on this honourable and necessarie resolution, hee returned with the selfe same silence, and warinesse wherewith hee came to his lodging, where griefe and anguish so wrung and op-pressed his surcharged heart, that without any further power to doe any thing, he fell downe in a swound upon his bed.

In this interim the day appeared, and caught these supposed new adulterers, intangled in the net of each others armes. *Marialonso* she awaked, and would have gone for that to *Loaysa,* which for the good service shee had done him, shee thought of right appertained unto her. But seeing that the day was now fully in, she was willing to deferre the receiving of her recompence, till the comming of the night.

Leonora was much troubled and perplexed, seing it was now broad day, cursing her owne carelessenesse, and that of her accursed Gover-nesse, whilest both of them with hastie steps hyed them thither where her husband was; praying to themselves as they went along, that they might finde him still snoring. And when they saw him lying on the bed, and not a word come from him, they did verily beleeve that the oyntment continued its working, since that he slept; and with great rejoycing, *Leonora* and *Marialonso* embraced each other.

Anon after, *Leonora* drew nigher and nigher to her husband, and taking hold of one of his armes, she turn'd him from the one side to the other, to try whether hee would awake, without putting her to the paines to wash him with vinegar, as she had beene told was needfull to bring him againe to himselfe. But with that tumbling and tossing of him too and fro, *Carrizales* returned from out his swounding, and fetching a deepe sigh, sayd with a lamentable weake voyce; Oh miserable and unfortunate man that I am! to what bad tearmes hath my fortune brought me!

Leonora did not well understand what her husband said, but as soon as she perceived that he was awake, and that he spake, wondring to see that the vertue of the oyntment did not last so long as was signified unto them; she came unto him, and laying her face to his, muching him with strickt embracements, shee sayd unto him; What ayl'st thou sweet-heart? me thinkes I heare you complaine as if you were not well.

The good old man heard the voice of his sweet enemie, and opening his eies in a wilde kinde of fashion like one amazed, and startled out of some fearefull dreame, he fixed them on her with great earnestnesse, and without moving the least haire of his eye-lids, he looked wissely and steadily on her a great while, and then at last he sayd unto her; Let me entreat thee (my deare) that you presently out of hand send for your father, and mother to come hither to mee, for I feele I know not what in my heart which does paine me exceedingly, and I feare it will speedily shorten my life; and I would feigne see them before I die.

Doubtlesse *Leonora* did certainely beleeve that what her husband sayd, was true; thinking that rather the strength of the oyntment, then that which hee had seene, had put him into this trance. And telling him, what he commanded should be done. She sent away *Luys* the *Negro,* willing him that he should forthwith go to her Parents, and hasten their speedy comming hither, for that the businesse required much haste, and their personall presence. Having dispatcht the messenger, she came to her Husband, embraced him, kissed him, and used towards him greater expressions of kindnesse then ever she had made show of heretofore; asking him how he did? where his griefe lay? and that with such tender and loving words, as if he had beene the onely thing in the world which she most loved and esteemed. He looked on her in the same kinde of wilde manner before mentioned; every word that she uttered, and every muching which she made of him, being a lance that smote him to the heart, and a sword that wounded his very soule.

In this meane while, the governesse had acquainted the servants of the house, and *Loaysa* with her Masters sicknes; indearing unto them, that it would quickly make an end of him, since that he had forgotten to command the doors towards the street to be shut, when the *Negro* went forth to call her Mistris Parents; wondring withall, why they should be sent for in such post-haste, since that neither of them had put their foot within that house, since they first married their Daughter.

In a word, they were all of them very silent, and knew not well what to make of it, none of them lighting on the true cause of their

Masters sicknesse, who ever and anone did fetch such deepe and dole-full sighes, as if every sigh would have broken his heart-strings, and rent up his soule by the roots from his bodie. *Leonora* wept to see him sigh in such sort, and he smiled to himselfe, like one that was not well pleased, considering the falshood of her teares.

Now by this time *Leonora's* Parents were come, and for that they found the doore to the street, and that to the inward Court open, and the house buried in silence, and no bodie to be seene, they wondred at it, and could not tell what to thinke of it, no small feares possessing their mindes, severall passions housing themselves in their distracted imaginations. Thus troubled, they went to their Sonne in Law's lodging, and found him (as already hath beene delivered) with his eies nailed to his wife, whom he held fast by the hand, both of them shedding many teares. She, on no other occasion, save seeing her husband shed them; and he, to see how feignedly his wife did let them fall.

As soone as her Parents were entred within the chamber, *Carrizales* saluted them, and sayd; I pray sit you down, and let all the rest voyd the roome, onely I will that the governesse *Marialonso* stay here; they did so. And onely these five remaining there without expecting that any body else should speake, in a low and soft voyce, (wiping first his eyes) *Carrizales* spake unto them after this manner.

I am well assured (dearest father and mother) that it shall not be needfull to bring any witnesses for to make you beleeve a truth, which I shall deliver unto you. You may very well remember (for it is not possible it should slippe out of your memory) with how much love, and with how great tendernesse a yeare now since, one moneth, five dayes, and nine houres, you delivered up unto me your beloved Daughter, to bee my lawfull wife. Yee likewise know what a great dowrie I made her; which was such, and in so liberall a manner, that three or foure of the same qualitie as her selfe, might therewith have beene married, with the opinion of rich. Yee may also call to minde the care and diligence I tooke in apparelling her, and adorning her with all that shee can desire or imagine; or that I could come to know was most fitting and convenient for her. In like manner (my very good friends) yee have seene, how carried away by mine owne naturall condition, and fearefull of that ill, which doubtlesse will bee my death; and experienced by reason of my great age, in the strange and various accidents of the world; I was desirous to keepe this Iewell which I had made choice of, and yee gave mee, with the greatest charinesse, and warinesse, as was possible for mee to doe. I raised up the walls of this house to a great heigth? I tooke away the sight and light from the windowes towards the streete; I made double lockes to the doores; I made such a *Tornell,* as they have at your Monasteries; I banished perpetually therefrom, all that which had but the shadow, or name ot man, or male-kinde. I gave her servants and slaves to attend her person; nor did I denie them, or her, ought that they did aske of mee; I made her my equall; I communicated with her my most secret thoughts, and made her Mistris of all my wealth and meanes. All these were such workes, being rightly and duely considered, as might have fully secured mee of enjoying of that without disturbance, which hath cost me so much; and that shee should have made it her studie, not to have given me any the least occasion of letting any kinde ot jealous feare to enter into my thought. But because the chasticement cannot bee prevented by humane diligence, which the divine will of Heaven is willing to inflict on those who doe not wholy place therein their desires, and hopes, it is no marvell that I remaine defrauded in mine. And that I my selfe have beene the Confectioner of that poyson, which now goes shortning and taking away my life. But because I perceiue the suspension wherein all of you stand, upon these words proceeding from my mouth; I will conclude the long preambles of this my discourse, with telling you in one word, that which is not possible to bee uttered in many thousands. I tell you then (my noble friends) that all that which I have sayd, and done, ends in this; that this woman I found (borne into the world, for the disturbing of my quiet, and losse of my life) (poynting to his wife) in the armes of a lusty young man, which is now secretly shut up in the lodging of this pestiferous Governesse.

Scarce had *Carrizales* ended these words, when as *Leonora* having her heart suddenly clouded, fell into a swound betweene her husbands knees. *Marialonso* lost her colour, and look't as pale as ashes; and *Leonora's* Parents had such a knot knit athwart their throats, that it would not give them leave to speake one word.

But *Carrizales* going on where hee left, sayd, the revenge which I purpose to take for this foule affront, is not, nor shall be such as ordinarily in the like cases are wont to bee taken. And therefore I will, that as I was extreame in that which I did; so likewise shall bee the vengeance which I will take, by taking it on my selfe, as most culpable in this offence. For I should, and ought to have considered with my selfe, that ill could agree and sort together the fifteene yeares of this young Woman, with the almost fourescore of mine; I was he, who like the Silke-worme, wrought the house wherein I must dye. Nor doe I blame thee ill advised young soule, (and in saying this, he bowed downe his head, and kissed the cheeke of *Leonora*) I doe not blame thee, I say; because the perswasions of subtill old Beldames, and the love-trickes of amorous young men, easily overcome and triumph over that little wit which thy few yeares afford. But because all the world may see and know the worth & value of that good will and affection wherewith I ever lov'd thee; in this last passage of my life, I will shew it in such sort, that it may remaine in the world for an example, if not of goodnesse, yet at least of such simplicitie of heart, as was never heretofore heard of, or seene. And therefore I will that a Scrivener be presently sent for, to make a new my last Will and

Testament; wherein I will double *Leonora's* Dowrie: and shall entreat her after my dayes are ended, which will bee but a few; that shee dispose her will (since that shee may then doe it without enforcing) to marry with that young man, whom the grey haires of this unfortunate old man never offended. And so shall shee see, that if living I did never goe one jot from that which I thought might give her content; now dying, I am desirous to doe the like; that she may take that felicitie with him whom shee seemeth to love so dearely. And to you (kinde Father and Mother) I will have a great care to leave you so well, and so rich, that you shall live plentifully during both your lives. The rest of my wealth shall goe to godly and pious uses. Cause the Scrivener to come presently unto mee, for the passion which hath alreadie taken hold of me, doth so oppresse and torment my heart, that it goes encreasing, and will in a very short time cut off the thread of my life.

Having sayd this, hee fell into a worse swounding then the former, and fell downe so neere to *Leonora,* that their faces were joyned each to other. A strange and sad spectacle for those her Parents, who with mournefull heart and eies looked on their beloved Daughter, and their kinde Sonne in Law. The naughty Governesse would not stay to receive the rebukes and the reprehensions, which she thought *Leonora's* Parents would bestow upon her; and therefore shee got her out of the lodging, and went to advertise *Loaysa* of all what had passed; advising him, to get him instantly out of the house, and that shee would take care to certifie him by the *Negro,* of the successe of this businesse, since that now there were no doores, nor keyes to hinder his passage. *Loaysa* was wonder-strucken with this strange newes, and following her counsell, returned to put on his old ragges like a poore beggar; and hastned to give an account to his friends of the successe of his love.

In the interim that those two were thus transported with their severall passions; *Leonora's* Father sent to call a Scrivener, an inward friend of his, who came just at that time that his Daughter and Son in Law were come againe to themselves. *Carrizales* made his Will in that forme and manner as wee told you before, without declaring *Leonora's* errour; more then that for some good respects, hee earnestly besought and entreated her that she would marry, in case he dyed, with that young man, whom he had told her of in secret.

When *Leonora* heard this, shee fell downe at her Husbands feet, and her heart panting within her breast, shee sayd unto him; Live (my deare husband, and my chiefest blisse) live many, many yeares. For albeit you are not bound to beleeve me in ought that I shall say unto you; know, that I have not offended you, save onely in thought; and beginning to excuse her selfe, and to recount at large the truth of the case; shee could not move her tongue to speake a word more, but fell anew into a swound.

Being in this dismayment, her grieved Husband embraced her; her loving Parents imbraced her; and all of them wept so bitterly, that they obliged, and even in a manner, inforced the Scrivener to accompanie them in their teares, who made the Testament. Wherein he left sufficient maintenance to all his houshold-servants; hee manumitted, and set at libertie his women-slaves, together with the *Negro*: but to false *Marialonso,* he bequeathed no more, but her bare wages.

Having thus settled his estate, the seventh day following, he was borne to his grave. *Leonora* remained a very sad and mournfull Widow, but was left very rich. And when as *Loaysa* well hoped, that shee would cumply with that (whereof he was not ignorant) which her Husband had recommended unto her in his Testament; but afterward saw, that within a seven-night after his death, she became a *Nunne,* and was admitted into one of the strictest Monasteries of all the Citie; being frustrated of his hopes, and ashamed to shew his face, lest hee should be made a laughing-stock, and by-word to all that knew him, he left *Sevill,* and went for the *Indyes.*

Leonora's Parents were full of sorow, and heavines, though some-what comforted with that, which their kind sonne in law had left them in his last Will, and Testament. The Maid-servants cheered themselves, as well as they could, with the liberall Legacies he had given them; And those his shee-slaves, together with *Luys* the *Negro,* rested the better satisfied with their infranchisement and freedome.

But that wicked, and accursed Governesse, shee was left (as she well deserved) very poore, and defrauded of all her evill thoughts, and lewd purposes. And I my selfe rest very well pleased, that I am now come to the end of this successe, Example, and Mirrour of the little confidence, which is to be put in Keyes, Locks, Tornells, and Walls, when as the will continueth free, and at libertie. And how much lesse we are to trust, and relye on greene and tender yeares, when are exhibited to their eares, the exhortations, and perswasions of such ill-disposed Governesses, whose habit and attyre is grave and Matron-like, but their tongues and hearts, full of deceit and mischiefe.

Only I doe not know what was the reason, that *Leonora* did not expresse her selfe more at large, in excusing her selfe, and in giving her jealous Husband to understand, how cleare, and unspotted shee was, and how cleare from doing him any wrong in that kind: but per-turbation, it should seeme, had knit a knot on her tongue, and the haste her Husband made to dye, did not give her time enough to make her just excuse.

THE LIBERALL LOVER

OH the lamentable Ruines of unhappie *Nicosia*! The bloud of thy valiant and unfortunate defenders being yet scarce drie. If (as thou art senselesse thereof) thou hadst any feeling at all in this desolate and woefull estate wherein now wee are, we might joyntly bewaile our misfortunes and that wretched estate and condition wherein wee are; And happily having a companion in them, it would help to ease mee in some sort of my torment, and make that burthen of my griefe the lighter; which I finde so heavie (I had almost sayd insupportable) for mee to beare. Yet there is some hope left unto thee, that these thy strong Towers dismantled and layd levell with the ground; thou mayst one day see them, (though not in so just a defence, as that wherein they were overthrowne) raised to their former height and strength.

But I, (of all unfortunate, the most unfortunate man,) what good can I hope for in that miserable straight wherin I finde my selfe? yea, though I should returne to the same estate and condition wherein I was, before I fell into this; such is my misfortune, that when I was free and at liberty, I knew not what happinesse was; and now in my thraldome and captivitie, I neither have it, nor hope it.

These words did a Christian Captive utter, looking with a sad and heavie countenance from the rising of a hill on the ruined Walls of the late lost *Nicosia*. And thus did he talke with them, and compared his miseries with theirs, as if they had beene able to understand him. (The common and proper condition of afflicted persons, who being violently carried away with their owne feigned fancies, and imaginary conceptions; doe, and say things beyond all reason, and without any good discourse, and advisement.)

Now whil'st hee was thus discoursing with himselfe from out a *Pavilion,* or one of those Tents pitched there in the field, not farre from

125

him issued out a *Turke,* a handsome young man, of a good presence, an ingenious aspect, and accompanied with spirit and mettall answer-able to his lookes; who drawing neere unto the *Christian,* without much ceremonie, yet in a fayre and civill way, sayd unto him; Sir, I durst lay a wager with you, that those your pensive thoughts which I read in your face have brought you hither. You read aright, answered *Ricardo,* (for this was the Captives name) they have brought mee hither indeed: But what doth it avayle mee? since in no place whether so ever I go, I am so farre from procuring a peace; that I cannot obtaine a truce, or any the least cessation of them. Nay rather these Ruines which from hence discover themselves unto mee, have rather increased my sorrowes. Those of *Nicosia* you meane? replied the *Turke;* What other should I meane (answered *Ricardo*) since there are no other which here offer themselves to my view. You have great cause (quoth the *Turke*) to weepe, if you entertaine your thoughts with these and the like contemplations.

For they, who but some two yeares since had seene this famous and rich Island of *Cyprus* in its prosperitie, and peaceable estate; the In-habitants thereof enjoying all that humane happines and felicitie, which the Heavens could grant unto men, or themselves desire, and now to see them banished out of it, or made miserable slaves in it; Who can bee so hard hearted, as to forbeare from bewailing its calamity and misfortune.

But let us leave talking of these things since they are remedilesse, and let us come to your owne bosome sorrowes, for I desire to see if they bee such, as you voyce them to bee. And therefore, I earnestly entreate and beseech you, and conjure thee, by that which thou owest to those good offices I have done thee; the good will I beare thee, the love I have showne thee, and by that which ought to obliege thee thereunto; in that wee are both of one and the same Country, and bred up in our Child-hood together; that thou wilt deale freely with me, and lay open unto me what is the cause which makes thee so exceeding sad and melancholy? For how be it, Captivity alone of it selfe bee sufficient to grieve the stoutest heart in the World, and to checke its mirth; though otherwise naturally inclined thereunto, yet notwithstanding I imagine, that the current of your disasters hath a farther reach and deeper bottome.

For generous minds (such as thine is) do not use to yeeld and render up themselves to common & ordinary misfortunes, in such a measure, as to make shew of extraordinary sorrowes. And I am the rather induced to beleeve what I conceive, because I know that you are not so poore, but that you are well enough able to pay any reasonable Ransome they shall require of you. Nor are you clapt up in the Towers of the blacke Sea, as a prisoner of note, or Captive of consideration, who late, or never obtaines his desired liberty. And therfore your ill fortune not having taken from you the hope of seeing your selfe a free man; and yet notwithstanding all this, when I see thee so much overcharged with sorrowes, and making such miserable manifestations of thy misfortunes; It is not much that I imagine that the paine proceeds from some other cause then thy lost liberty, which I entreat thee to acquaint mee withall; offering thee all the assistance I am able to give thee. Perhaps, to the end that I may be serviceable unto thee, Fortune in her wheeling hath brought this about, that I should bee clad in this habite which I so much hate and abhorre.

Thou knowest already (*Ricardo*) that my Master is *Cadi* of this Citie (which is the same, as to be it's *Bishop*;) Thou likewise knowest the great sway which he beareth here, and how much I am able to do with him. Together with this, thou art not ignorant of the fervent desire and inflamed zeale which I have, not to dye in this estate which I thus seeme to professe; but God knowes my heart, and if ever I should come to be put to my tryall, I am resolved openly to confesse, and in a loud voice to publish to the whole world, the Faith of

Iesus Christ, from which my few yeares, and lesse understanding separated mee; though that I were sure that such a confession should cost mee my life; for that I may free my selfe from losing that of my soule, I should thinke the losing of that of my body very well employed.

Out of all this which hath beene sayd unto thee, I leave it to thy selfe to inferre the conclusion, and that thou wilt take it into thy deeper and better consideration; whether my proffered friendship may be proffitable and usefull unto thee.

Now that I may know what remedies thy misfortune requires, and what medicines I may apply both for the easing and curing of it; it is requesite, that thou recount it unto mee; the relation thereof being as necessary for me, as that of the rich Patient to his Phisitian; assuring thee in the faith of a friend, that thou shalt deposite it in the deepest and darkest den of silence, never to come to light.

To all these words of his, *Ricardo* gave an attentive eare, though his tongue were silent; but seeing himselfe oblieged by them and his owne necessity, returned him thereunto this answer.

If as thou hast hit the right veine Oh my dear friend *Mahamut* (for so was this *Turke* called) touching that which thou imaginest of my misfortune, thou couldst hit as right upon its remedy; I should hold my selfe happy in my lost liberty, and would not change my unhappines, for the greatest happines that may be imagined. But I wott well, that it is such, that all the World may take notice of the cause whence it proceedeth; but that man cannot therin be found, which dare undertake not onely the finding out of any remedy for it, but of giving it any the least ease. And to the end that thou mayst rest thy selfe throughly satisfied of the truth therof, I will relate the same unto thee, as briefly and compendiously as I can, shutting up much in a few words. But before I enter into this confused laborinth of my miseries; I would first have thee to recount unto mee, what is the cause why

S

Azam Bashawe my master hath pitched here in this field these *Tents* and *Pavilions,* before hee maketh his entry into *Nicosia,* being deputed (and to that purpose bringing his provision with him) to bee *Viceroy* there, or *Bashawe,* the useuall stile or title which the *Turks* give their *Viceroy's.*

I will (answered *Mahamut*) answer your demand in a few words; and therefore would have you to know, that it is a custome amongst the *Turks,* that they who come to be *Viceroyes* of some *Province,* do not instantly enter into the Citie where their Predecessor resideth, till he issueth out of it, and leave the residence freely to his Successors. Now when the new *Bashawe* hath made his entrance, the old one stayes without in the field, expecting what accusations shal come against him, and what misdemeanours (during his government) they shall lay to his charge; which being alleadged and proved, are recorded, and a note taken of them, all possibility being taken away from him of enterviewing, either to help himself by suborning of witnesses, or by his friends, unles he have made his way before hand, for the clearing of himselfe. Now the other being setled in his *Residence,* there is given by him to him that leaves his *Charge,* a scroll of Parchment sealed up very close, and therewith he presents himselfe at the gate of the *Grand-Signior;* that is to say, in the Court before the *Grand-Councell* of the great *Turke;* which being seene and perused by the *Visir-Bashaw,* and by those other foure inferiour *Bashawes;* they either reward, or punish him, according to the relation that is made of his *Residencie:* In case that he come home faulty, with money he redeems and excuseth his punishment: but if faultlesse, and they do not reward him (as commonly it falleth out) with gifts and presents, he procureth that *Charge* which himselfe most affecteth. For places of command and offices are not given for merit, but for money, all is sold, and all bought. They who have the Provision, (or as we stile it, commission and authoritie for the conferring of charges and offices,) robbe those which are to have these offices and charges, and fleece them as neare as the sheeres can goe. And they again out of this their bought office, gather wealth and substance for to buy another, which promiseth much more gaine. All goes as I tell you, all this Empire is violent, a signe that it will not last long. For that reason then that I have rendred thee, thy master *Azam Bashawe* hath remained in this field foure dayes; and he of *Nicosia,* that he hath not as yet come forth as he ought to have done; the cause is, that he hath been very sicke, but is now upon the mending hand; and will without faile come forth either to day or to morrow at the farthest; and is to lodge in certain Tents which are pitcht behind this rising hill, which as yet thou hast not seene; and thy master is forthwith to enter into the Citie. And having made this already delivered, known unto thee, is all the satisfaction that I can give to your propounded demaund.

Listen then unto mee, replied *Ricardo*; but I know not whether I shall be as good as my word, in cumplying with that which I formerly promised; that I would in a few words recount unto you my misfortunes, they being so large, that to make up the full measure of them, I want words enough to do it; yet notwithstanding, I wil do herein what may be, and as time and your patience will permit.

But let me first of all aske you, if you know in our town of *Trapana,* a *Damosell* to whom *Fame* hath given the name of the fairest woman in all *Sicily*; in whose praise all curious tongues have spent themselves, and of whom the rarest judgements have ratified, that she was the perfectest peece of beauty that the past age had, the present hath, and that which is to come can hope to have; one of whom the Poets sang, that her haires were golden wyars, her eyes, two resplendent Suns; and her cheeks, pure damask-roses; her teeth, Pearles; her lips, Rubies; her necke, Alablaster; and that her parts with the whole frame, and the whole with her parts, made up a most pleasing harmony, and most harmonious concord. Nature spreading over the whole com-

131

posure such a sweet delightfulnesse of colours, so naturall, and so perfect, that envie it selfe cannot taxe her in any one particular.

And is it possible (*Mahamut*) that all this while thou hast not told
me yet who shee is, and by what name she is called? I undoubtedly
beleeve, that either thou dost not heare mee, or that when thou wast
in *Trapana,* thou didst want thy sences. *Mahamut* hereunto answered;
that if shee whom thou hast set forth with such extreames of beauty
bee not *Leonisa,* the Daughter of *Rodolphus Florencius,* I know not who
shee is; for shee alone had that fame which you speake of.

This is she, oh *Mahamut* (replied *Ricardo*) this is she (oh my deare
friend) who is the principall cause of all my felicity, and of all my
misfortune. This is shee, and not my lost libertie, for whom mine
eyes have, do, and shall shed teares not to bee numbered; This is shee,
for whom my heart-burning sighes inflame the ayre farre and neere:
And this is shee, for whom my words weary heaven, which heares
them, and the eares of those which hearken unto them. This is shee,
for whom thou tookest mee to be mad, or at least, for a man of small
worth, and lesse courage. This *Leonisa,* to me a Lyonesse, and to
another a meeke and gentle Lambe; is shee which holds mee in this
wretched and miserable estate.

For I must give thee to understand, that from my tender yeares, or
at least, ever since I had the use of reason, I did not onely love, but
adore her; and did serve her with such solicitude and devotion, as if
neither on earth, nor in Heaven there were any other Deitie for mee
to serve and adore, save her selfe.

Her kinsfolke and Parents knew my desires, considering withall,
that they were directed to an honest and vertuous end. And that
therefore, many a time and oft (which escaped not my knowledg)
they acquainted *Leonisa* with the fervent love and affection I bare unto
her, for the better disposing of her will to accept mee for her Husband.

But shee, who had placed her eyes on *Cornelio,* the Sonne of

Ascanio Rotulo, (whom you know very well) a young Gallant, neate and spruce, with white hands, and curled haires, having a melifluous voice, and amorous words at will; and in a word, being all made of *Amber, Muske,* and *Civet,* clad in *Tissue,* adorned with rich embroy-deries,) would not vouchsafe to caſt so much as one glaunce of her eye on my countenance, which was not so delicate as that of *Cornelio,* neither would entertaine (notwithſtanding my beſt endeavours to please her) with thankefulnesse, my many and continuall services, requiting my good will with disdaine and hatred: And to such extreames did the excesse of my love bring mee, that I should have held my selfe happie, had her disdaines and unkindnesses kil'd me outright, that I might not have liv'd to have seene her conferre such open, though honeſt favours on *Cornelio.* Consider now, being anguished with disdaine and hatred, and almoſt mad with the cruell rage of jealousie, in what miserable case (you may imagine) my soule was, two such mortall plagues reigning therein. *Leonisa's* Parents dis-sembled those favours which she did to *Cornelio;* beleeving (as they had good reason to beleeve it,) that the young man attraĉted by her moſt exquesite and incomparable beautie (which none could match, but her owne) would make choice of her for his Spouse, and so in him gaine a richer sonne in Law, then in me: and well (if he were so) might he be so. But I dare be bold to say, (without arrogancie be it spoken) that as good bloud runs in my veines, as his; my quality and condition nothing inferiour to his; and for his minde, it cannot bee more noble then mine, nor his valour goe beyond mine: But that indeed which did over ballance mee, was *Leonisa's* favour, and her Parents furthering the businesse; and this onely made the scales un-even, by their enclining to *Cornelio.*

Now it so fell out, that persiſting in the pursuite of my pretensions, it came to my knowledge, that one day in the moneth of *May* laſt paſt, which this very day makes up a yeare, three dayes, and five houres; *Leonisa,* her Parents, and *Cornelio,* and some friends of his, went to solace themselves, accompanied with their kindred, and servants to *Ascanio* his Garden, neare adjoyning to the Sea-side, in the way that leads to the Salt-pits.

I know that place passing well (sayd *Mahamut,*) goe on *Ricardo;* I was more then foure dayes in one of them, I could have wisht I had beene there but foure minutes.

I knew that (replied *Ricardo*) and in that very instant that I knew it, my soule was possessed with such a fury, such a rage, and such a hell of jealousies, and with that vehemencie and rigour, that it bereaved mee of my senses, as thou shalt plainely, by that which I presently did see, which was this.

I hyed mee to the Garden where I was told they were, where I found most of the company solasing themselves, and *Cornelio* & *Leonisa* sitting under a Walnut-tree somewhat out of the way from the rest. How my sight pleased them I doe not know, but know, to say so much of my selfe, that her sight wrought so upon mee, that I lost the sight of mine owne eyes; and stood stocke still like a *Statua,* without either voice, or motion. But I continued not long so, before that my anger awakened my choler, choler, heated my bloud; my bloud, inflamed rage; and rage gave motion to my hands, and tongue. Howbeit my hands were bound by the respect which (me'thought) was due to that fayre face which I had before mee; But my tongue breaking silence, vented forth these words;

How canst thou finde in thy heart, how give thy selfe content (Oh thou mortall enemie of my rest) in having, (and therin taking so much pleasure) before thine eyes, the cause which must make mine to overflow with rivers of teares; and by my continuall weeping, become another Deluge? Come, come, (cruell as thou art) a little nearer, and wreathe thy twining Ivie, about this unprofitable truncke, which wooes thy embracings. Let him lay his head in thy lap, and let thy

fingers learne to play with those breaded lockes of this thy new *Ganimede*; what thou wilt doe, doe quickly; Make an end at once of delivering up the possession of thy selfe, to the greene and ungoverned yeares of this your *Minion*; to the end, that I losing all hope of obtaining thee; may together with that, end this my life, so much by mee abhorred.

Thinkst thou peradventure (thou proud and ill advised Damosell) that this young *Princoxe,* presumptuous by reason of his riches; arrogant, by your gracing of him, unexperienced, in that hee is too young; and insolent by his relying on his Linage, will love as he ought, and you deserve? No, hee cannot, no, hee knowes not how to love constantly; nor to esteeme that which is inestimable, nor come to have that under-

135

ſtanding and knowledge, which accompanies ripe and experimented yeares. If you thinke so, doe not thinke it; for the World hath no other good thing, save the doing of its actions alwaies after one and the same manner. For none are deceived, but by their owne ignorance: In yong men there is much inconſtancie; in rich, pride; vanitie in the arrogant; in the beautifull, disdaine; and in those that have all these, foolishnesse, which is the mother of all ill successe.

And thou (oh young Gallant) art such a one, who thinkſt to carry all before thee, and to goe cleare away with that reward, which is more due to my good desires, then thy idle proteſtations; Why doſt thou not arise from that Carpet of flowers whereon thou lyeſt, and come to take this my soule from me, which so deadly hateth thine? Not because thou offendeſt me in that which thou doeſt, but because thou knoweſt not how to eſteeme that good which fortune gives thee: and it is cleare and evident, that thou makſt little reckoning of it, since thou wilt not rise up to defend it, that thou mayſt not put thy selfe to the hazzard of discomposing that painted composure of thy gay cloathes. If *Achilles* had had thy reposed condition, or beene of thy cold temper; *Vlysses* might very well have beene assured, that he would not have gone through with that which hee undertooke. Go, get thee gone and sport thy selfe amongſt thy Mothers mayds, and there have a care of kembing and curling thy lockes, and keeping thy hands cleane and white; thou art fitter to handle soft silks, then a hard hilted sword.

All these words could not move *Cornelio* to rise from the place where I found him, but sate him ſtill looking upon mee as one agaſt, not once offering to ſtirre. But the voice wherewith I uttered these words which you have heard, occasioned the people which were walking in the garden to draw nearer, ſtood a little while liſtening, hearing many other disgracefull speeches which I gave him, and thereupon made in; who taking courage by their comming (for all or most of them were his kinsfolke, servants, or friends) hee made show of rising; but before he was fully upon his feete, I layd hand on my sword, drew it, and did set not onely upon him, but on as many as were there. *Leonisa* no sooner saw my glittering sword, but shee fell into a deadly swound, which did put greater courage into mee, and stirre up greater despighte: and I cannot say, whether those so many which did set upon mee, sought onely to defend themselves, as we see men usually doe against a furious mad man; or whether it were my good fortune and diligence, or Heavens disposing, to expose me to greater evills, and to reserve mee to farther miseries. In conclusion, I wounded seven or eight of them which came next to my hand; *Cornelio* betooke himselfe to his heeles, and by his swift flight escaped my hands.

Being in this so manifest a danger hemmed in by my enemies, who now (seeing their bloud runne from them, and inraged with the wrong which they had received) sought to revenge themselves upon mee: Loe *Fortune* provided a remedie for this mischiefe, but such a one as was worse than the disease; for better had it beene for mee there to have left my life, then in restoring it mee by so strange and unexpected a meanes, to come to lose it every houre a thousand and a thousand times over and over. And this it was; That on the sodaine there rushed into the garden a great number of *Turkes,* Pirates of *Viserta,* who with two Gallies had put into a little Creeke of the Sea, betweene two rockes hard by the shoare, where they disimbarked themselves without being heard or seene by the *Centinells* of the Watch-Towers, nor discovered by those scouts, whose dayly office it was to scoure the Coasts, and see that all was cleare. When my adversaries had espied them, leaving me alone; they, with the rest in the garden, ranne their way as fast as their legs would carry them, and shifted so well for themselves, that they had got themselves out of their danger, and put themselves in safetie. So that of all the whole companies, the *Turkes*

T

tooke no more Captives, but three persons besides *Leonisa,* who lay there still in a swound. They tooke me after they had shrewdly wounded me in foure severall places, revenged before by me on foure *Turkes* whom I left dead in the place.

This assault ended, the *Turks* with their accustomed diligence, and not being very well pleased with the successe; made haste to embarke themselves, and presently put farther to sea, so that what with their sailes, and help of their Oares, in a short space they recovered *Fabiana;* where they mustered their men, and finding that the slaine were foure souldiers, *Levant-men* (as they call them,) being of the best and choisest, and of most esteem amongst them, they were the more willing and desirous to take their revenge of me. And therefore the *Admirall* of the Captaine-galley commanded them to hang me up on the mayn yard. All this while *Leonisa* stood looking on this speedy preparation for my death, (who was now come again to her selfe) and seeing me in the power of these *Pirats,* the teares trickled down in great abundance from her beauteous eyes, and wringing her soft and delicate hands, not speaking so much as one word; gave diligent eare and was very attentive to hear if she could understand what the *Turkes* said. But one of the *Christian-slaves* that was chained to the Oare, spake to her in *Italian,* giving her to understand how that the Captaine had given order to have that *Christian* hanged up (pointing unto me) because I had slaine in her defence, foure of the best souldiers belonging to his Galleys. Which being heard and understood by *Leonisa;* (being the first time that ever shee shew'd her selfe pittifull towards me) she will'd the sayd slave that he should speake unto the *Turkes* to spare his life, and not to hang him; for in so doing they would lose a great ransome, and that he should advise them to tack about, and make againe for *Trapana,* where his ransome would presently be brought aboord unto them. This I say was the first, and the last kindnesse which *Leonisa* used towards mee, and all this for my greater ill. The

Turks hearing what their Captive told them, did easily beleeve him; and this their hope of profit, turned the course of their choller. The very next morning hanging out a flag of peace, they anchored before *Trapana.* That night thou maist better conceive then I utter, with what a deale of griefe I past it over; not so much for my wounds sake, though they were very sore and painfull, as to thinke on the perill wherein my cruell enemie was amongst these *Barbarous* people. Being come now as I told thee to the Citie, one of the Galleys entred the Haven, the other stood off. All the Citizens flocked to the sea-side, the *Christians* standing as thicke one by another, as the shoare would give them leave. And that Carpet-knight *Cornelio* stood afar off observing what passed in the Galley, whil'st my Steward was treating of my ransome; to whom I had given order that he should in no wise treate of my liberty, but of that of *Leonisa:* and that he should give for the freeing of her, all whatsoever I was worth, either in lands, or goods. And I willed him moreover, that hee should goe a shoare and tell *Leonisa's* Parents, that they should leave it to him to treate of their Daughters liberty.

This being done, the chiefe Captain who was a *Grecian,* but a *Renegado,* his name *Ysuph,* demanded for *Leonisa,* 6000 Crownes, and for my selfe foure thousand, and that hee would not sell the one without the other; setting this so great a prise (as I was given after-wards to understand) because he was enamoured of *Leonisa,* and was therefore unwilling she should be redeemed; purposing to give to the Captaine of the other Galley (with whom he was to share the one halfe of the prize) my selfe at the rate of 4000 Crownes in ready money, and 1000 more in other commodities, which made up 5000, prizing *Leonisa* at other 5000. And this was the reason why he rated us two in ten thousand Crownes. *Leonisa's* Parents offered him nothing on their part, relying on the promise which on my part my Steward had made them; neither did *Cornelio* so much as once open his lips to offer any thing towards her ransome. And so after many demaunds and answers, my Steward concluded the businesse, with giving for *Leonisa* 5000, and for mee 3000 Crownes. *Ysuph* accepted this offer, forced thereunto by the perswasions of his companion, and all the reft of their Souldiers. But because my Steward had not so much money in Cash, hee entreated onely three daies time to make up the full summe, with intention to sell my goods under hand, and at a cheape rate, till he had got so much together as would pay the ransome. *Ysuph* was glad of this, thinking with himselfe in the mean while to finde some occasion that the bargaine might not goe forward; and so returning backe againe to the Island of *Fabiana,* he sayd, that by that time the three dayes were expired, he would not faile to be there with them, to receive the money according to the agreement.

But spitefull and ungratefull *Fortune,* not yet wearied out with ill entreating mee; had so ordained it, that a Gallies boy who sate on the top of the maft, as the *Turkes Centinell* discovered afarre off at Sea, sixe *Italian* Gallies, and did guesse (which was true) that they were either of *Malta,* or *Sicily.* Hee came running downe with all the hafte hee could to give them newes thereof; and in a trice the *Turkes* embarked themselves, who were a shoare, some dressing their dinner, some washing their linnen; and weighing anchor in an inftant, hoysing saile, and working hard with their Oares, turning their Prows to-wards *Barbary*; in lesse then two houres, they loft the sight of those Gallies, and so being shadowed with the Island, and covered from kenne by the approaching night, they were secured from that feare which afrighted them.

Now I leave it to thy good consideration (my friend *Mahamut*) how much my minde was troubled in this voyage, finding it to fall out so crosse and contrary to that which I expected: and much more, when the next day the two Gallies reaching the Island of *Pantanalea* on the South part, the *Turks* went a shoare to get them wood, and fresh victuals; but moſt of all, when I saw both the Captaines land, and fell to sharing between them in equall proportion all those prizes they had taken, each action of these, was to mee a delayed death. Comming then at laſt to the dividing of my selfe, and *Leonisa*; *Ysuph* gave to *Fetala*, (for so was that Captaine of the other Galley called) sixe *Chriſtians*, foure for the Oare, and two very beautifull boyes, both naturalls of *Corso*, and my selfe likewise with them, that hee might have *Leonisa* for himselfe. Wherewith *Fetala* reſted very well con- tented. And albeit I were present at all this, I could not undeſtrand what they sayd, though I knew what they did; neither had I known then the manner of their sharings, if *Fetala* had not come unto mee and told mee in *Italian*; *Chriſtian* thou art now mine, and put into my hands (as my Captive) thou being rated as two thousand Crownes; if thou wilt have thy libertie, thou muſt give mee 4000, or resolve here to end thy daies. I then demanded of him, whether the *Chriſtian* Damosell were his too, he told mee no, but that *Ysuph* kept her for himselfe, with intention to make her turne *Moore*, and then marrie her. And therein he sayd true; for one of the Galley slaves told mee, that sate chained on his bancke at his Oare, and underſtood very well the *Turkish* language, that hee over-heard *Ysuph* and *Fetala* treating therof. Whereupon I came to my maſter and told him, Sir; if you will bring the businesse so about that the *Chriſtian* Damosell may be- come your Captive, I will give you ten thousand Crownes in good gold for her ransome. He replied, it was not possible; but I will acquaint *Ysuph* with this great summe which thou offereſt for her freedome: and perhaps, weighing the profit he shall reape thereby, hee will alter his purpose, and accept of the ransome. Hee did so; and then presently commanded all those of his own Galley to em- barke themselves as soone as possibly they could, because he would goe for *Tripoli* in *Barbarie*, whence he was. And *Ysuph* likewise deter- mined to goe for *Viserta*; and so embarked with the selfe same haſte as they use to doe when they kenne either Galleys which they feare, or *Vessells* which they minde to robbe. And that which moved them to make the more haste, was; that they saw the weather began to change, with manifest signes of a storme.

Leonisa was on land, but not there where I might see her, save onely at the time of her embarking, where wee both met at the sea-side. This her new lover led her by the hand, and setting her foot upon the planke which reached from the land to the Galley; she turned backe her eyes to looke upon mee, and mine, which never were off from her, looked wishly on her, but with such tendernesse; that without knowing how such a cloud was cast before them, that it took away my eye-sight; and being robb'd of it, and of my senses, I fell in a swound to the ground. The like they afterwards told mee befell *Leonisa*; for they saw her fall from the planke into the Sea, and that *Ysuph* leapt in after her, and brought her out thence in his armes. This was told mee by those of my masters Galley whereinto they had put me, I not knowing how I came there.

But when I came againe to my selfe, and saw my selfe alone in that Galley, and the other steering a contrary course, and gone cleane out of sight from us, carrying away with them the one halfe of my soule, or (to say better) all of it; my heart was clouded anew, and I began anew to curse my misfortune, and called out aloud for death. And such, and so great was the moane and lamentation I made, that my masters eares being offended therewith, threatned with a great cudgell, that if I did not hold my peace, he would severely punish me. Whereupon I repressed my teares, and smothered my sighes, thinking that the violent restraining of them, would breake out the more forceably in some one part or other, and open a doore to let my soule out, which I so earnestly desired, might relinquish this my miserable body. But froward Fortune not contenting her selfe to have put mee into this so narrow a streight, tooke a course to overthrow all, by taking from me

all hope of remedie; for in an inſtant, the ſtorme wee so much feared overtooke us, and the Wind which blew ſtrongly from the *South,* blew full in the teeth of us; and began with such furie to re-inforce it selfe, that wee were forced to tacke about, putting the Prow in the Poopes place, suffering our Galley to goe which way the winde would carry her.

Our Captaines designe was, by fetching of boords, to have put into some part of the Island for shelter; and more particularly, on the *North* part thereof: but it fell not out answerably to his expeﬔation, but rather quite contrary to what hee had designed; for the winde charged us with such impetuousnesse, that all that which we had sayled in two dayes, within little more then foureteene houres, we saw our selves within two Leagues or thereabout of the same Island from whence hee had put forth; And now there was no remedy for hindring our being driven upon it, and not to runne our selves upon some sandy-shoare, but amongſt very high Rocks, which presented themselves to our view, threatning inevitable death to our lives.

Wee saw on the t'one side of us, that other our fellow Galley wherein was *Leonisa,* and all their *Turkes,* and Captive-rowers labour-ing hard with their oares, to keep themselves off as well as they could from running upon the Rockes. The like did wee in ours, but with better successe (it should seeme) and greater force and ſtrength then the other; who being tyred out with their travaile, and overcome by the ſtiffenesse of the winde, and bluſtering ſtorme; forsaking their Oares, and with them abandoning themselves, they suffered them-selves (wee looking upon them) to fall amongſt the Rockes, againſt which the Galley dashing it selfe, was split in a thousand peeces.

Night was then drawing on, and so great was the cry of those that gave themselves for loſt; and the fright of those who in our Vessell feared to bee loſt, that not any one of those many things which our Captaine commanded, was either underſtood, or done by them; onely they did attend the not forgoing of their Oares, plying them still, holding it for their best remedie to turne the Prow to the Winde, and to cast two Anchors into the Sea to keep off death for a while, which they held to bee certaine. And although the feare of dying was generall in all of them, yet in mee was it quite contrary; for fed with the deceit﹣full hope of seeing her in that other World, who was so lately departed out of this; every minute that the Galley deferred its drowning, or splitting against the Rockes, was to mee an age of a more painefull death. The high swollen waves which past over the toppe of our weather beaten Vessell, and my head; made mee very watchfull to see whether or no, I could espie floating upon those crump shouldered billowes, the bodie of unfortunate *Leonisa*.

But I will not detaine my selfe now (O *Mahamut*) in recounting unto thee peece by peece, the passions, the feares, the anguishes, the thoughts, which in that tedious and terrible night I had, and passed; that I may not goe against that which before I propounded, and promised, in relating briefly unto thee my misfortune. Suffice it, that they were such and so great, that if death had come to me at that time, hee needed not to have taken any great paines in taking away my life.

Day appeared, but with appearance of a farre greater storme then the former; and wee found that our Vessell lay riding out at Sea, and a good waies off from the Rocks. And having descried a point of the Island, and perceiving that wee might easily double it, both *Turkes,* and *Christians* began to bee of good cheare, taking new hopes, and new hearts unto them, fell anew to their worke, in sixe houres we doubled the point, and found the Sea more calme and quiet; insomuch, that with a great deale more ease, they could handle and use their Oares; and comming under *Lee* of the Island, the *Turkes* leapt out to land, and went to see if there were any reliques remaining of the Galley which the night before fell on the Rockes. But even then too would not *Fortune* bee so favourable unto mee, as to give me that poore com﹣

fort which I hoped to have had of seeing *Leonisa's* bodie in these my armes; which though dead and broken, I would have beene glad to have seene it, for to breake that impossibilitie which my starre had put upon mee, of linking my selfe therewith, as my desires well deserved. And therefore entreated one of the *Renegadoes* to dis-embarke himselfe to goe in search thereof, and to see if the rolling of the Sea had cast her on the shoare. But (as I told thee) all this did Heaven deny me; and just in that very instant the Winde began to rise, and the Sea grow rough, so that the shelter of that Island was not of any benefit at all unto us.

Fetala seeing this, would not strive against *Fortune,* who had so violently persecuted him; and therefore commanded them to right and fit the Galley to beare a little sayle, & to turn the Prow to the Sea-ward, and the Poope to the Wind-ward; and he himselfe taking charge of the Rudder, sate at the helme, suffering her to runne through the wide Sea; being well assured that no impediment would crosse its course: The Oares bare themselves very eeven, being seated very orderly on their bankes, and all the rest of the company got them into the Hold underneath the Hatches, so that there was not a man to bee seene on the Deck, save the Master; who for his more safety, caused himselfe to be bound fast to his seate, giving thence direction to the Rowers, for the better governing and guiding of the Vessell; which made its way with that swiftnesse, that in three dayes, and three nights, passing in sight of *Trapana,* of *Melazo,* and *Palermo,* she imboked by the *Pharos* of *Mecina,* to the wonderfull feare of those that were in her, and of those likewise which behold them on the land.

In fine, not to bee tedious in recounting unto thee the terriblenesse of this tempest, which is beyond all expression, I say; that being weary, hungry, and tyred out with such a large compasse about, as was the rounding of almost all the whole Island of *Sicily,* wee arrived at *Tripoli* in *Barbarie*; where my master (before that he had reckoned with his *Levant-men,* shared out the spoiles, and given that unto them which was their due, and a fifth to the King, as the custome is;) fell sicke of a Pluresie, accompanied with a burning Fever in that violent manner, that within three dayes it sent him packing to hell.

The King of *Tripoli* seazed presently upon all his goods; and the *Alacade de los muertos,* which is an Office of Inquirie concerning the dead, substituted by the great *Turke*; who as you know, is heire to those that are his naturall Subjects after their deaths. These two possessed themselves of all my Master *Fetala's* wealth, and I fell into the hands of him who was the *Viceroy* of *Tripoli*; and within fifteen daies after he received his Patent for *Cyprus,* with whom (you see) I am come hither, but without any intention at all to ransome my selfe, though he hath often told me that I should if I would, and wondred why I did not do it all this while, being (as *Fetala's* Souldiers told him) a principall person, and a man of good meanes in his owne Countrey. But I was so far from entertaining that motion, that I told him, that they had misinformed him of my fortunes. And if thou wilt (*Mahamut*) that I acquaint thee truely with what I thinke; Know thou then, that I will never returne backe againe to that place, where I can no waies receive any comfort, and where *Leonisa's* death will in part, if not wholy bee imputed unto mee. What pleasure then can I take, either there, or here; in this my thraldome, though I must confesse, that the remembrance of her losse is more grievous unto mee then a thousand Captivities. And if it bee true, that continuall sorrowes, must of force have an end, or end him who suffers them; mine cannot choose but doe it, for I am resolved to give them such a loose reine, that within a few dayes, they shall give an end to this my miserable life, which I hold so much against my will.

This (O my brother *Mahamut*) is my sad successe; This is the cause of these my sighes and teares; Behold now and consider, if this bee not sufficient for to hale the one from out the deepest bottome of my bowels, and to exhale the other from out my afflicted and tormented bosome? *Leonisa* is dead, and with her my hope; and though that which I had (she living) hung but by a small and slender thread; yet, yet, and with this yet, his tongue clave so close to the roofe of his mouth, that he could not speake one word more, nor refraine from weeping, whose teares, drop after drop, one overtaking another, trickled downe his face in such abundance, that the ground was all wet whereon they fell. *Mahamut,* accompanied those with his teares.

But this *Parosisme* being over-past, caused by relating this sad story, and calling to minde his lost *Leonisa*; *Mahamut* was very willing, and withall went about to comfort him all that he could, with as good terms and perswasions as possibly he could deuise. But *Ricardo* did cut him short of telling him.

That which thou art (my deare friend) to do, is; that thou wilt advise me, what course I shall take for to fall into disgrace with my master, and with all those with whom I shall converse, that being hated and abhorred by him, and by them; the one and the other might ill entreate me, and persecute me in such sort, that adding sorrow to sorrow, I may speedily obtain that which I so earnestly desire, which is, to end my life.

Now I finde that to bee true (sayd *Mahamut*) which is commonly spoken; *Lo que se sabe sentir, se sabe dezir.* He that knowes his griefe, knows how to speak it; though sometimes it so happeneth that it maketh the tongue dumbe. But howsoever it bee, (whether thy sorrowes reach to thy words, or thy words out goe thy sorrowes) thou shalt ever (*Ricardo*) finde me thy true friend, either for assistance, or for counsaile. For albeit my few yeares, and the inconsideratnesse which I have committed, in putting my selfe into this habit, may cry out against mee that of neither of these two things which I offer thee, thou mayst have any confidence, or hope; yet will I endeavour to the utmost of my power, that this suspition may not prove true, nor any such opinion be held for certaine. And albeit thou wilt not neither bee advised, nor assisted by me, yet wil I not leave off doing that which shall be fitting and convenient for thee; as good Phisitians use to deale with their sicke patients, who doe not give them that which they crave, but what they thinke convenient for them to have.

There is not any in all this Citie, that can doe, or prevaile more then the *Cadi* my Master; no, not even thine, (who comes to bee *Viceroy* thereof) is so powerfull as hee. This being so as it is, I dare be bold to say, that I am the man that can doe most in this Citie, because I can doe whatsoever I will with my Master. I speake this, because it may bee I shall so plot the businesse with him, and bring it so handsomely about, that thou mayst come to bee his; and being in my company, time will teach us that which we are to doe, as well for to comfort thee, if thou wilt or canst bee comforted, as likewise for my selfe to get out of this, to a better life; or at least, to some place where it may be more safe when I leave this. I kindly thanke you (*Mahamut*) replied *Ricardo* for your proffered friendshippe, though sure I am, that when thou hast done all thou canst do, thou canst not do any thing that can do me any good.

But let us now give over this discourse, and make towards the Tents; for if my eye-sight deceive me not, I see a great presse of people comming out of the Citie, and doubtlesse it is the old *Viceroy*, who comes forth into the field for to give place unto my Master, that hee may enter the Citie, to make his *Residence*. It is even so, sayd *Mahamut*, come along with mee *Ricardo*, and thou shalt see the Ceremonies wherewith they receive him, for I know thou wilt take pleasure in seing them. With a very good will answered *Ricardo*; for peradventure I shall have need of thee; if happily the *Guardian* of my Masters Captives should happen to meet with mee, who is a *Renegado*, and by birth of *Corso*, but of no very pittifull and tender bowels.

Here they left off any farther communication, and came to the

149

Tents just at that very instant as the old *Bashawe* came thither; and the new one came forth to receive him at the doore of the Tent. *Ali Bashaw,* (for so was he called who left the government) came accompanied with all the *Ianizaries,* being the ordinary garrison Souldiers in *Nicosia,* ever since the *Turkes* were masters of it, being to the number of five hundred. They came in two Wings or Files; the one with their Muskets, and the other with naked *Simyters.* They came to the Tent of the new *Bashaw Hazan,* rounding it from one side at the doore thereof, till they met at the other; where *Ali Bashaw* bowing his body, made a lowly reverence to *Hazan;* and he with a lesse enclining himselfe, re-saluted him.

This done *Ali* presently entred into *Hazan's* Pavillion, where the *Turkes* presently mounted him upon a proud Horse, with wondrous rich furniture; and conducting him round about the Tents, and a good part of the field, clamouring out with loud acclamations in their owne language; Long live *Solyman Sultan,* and *Hazan Bashaw* in his name: They repeated this very often, re-inforcing their voices and vociferations, and then presently returned back againe to the ·Tent, where *Ali Bashaw* remained; who with the *Cadi* and *Hazan,* shut themselves up close for the space of one houre all alone: *Mahamut* then told *Ricardo,* that they had thus retyred themselves, to treat of that which was fit to be done in the Citie, touching such businesses as were commenced, but not finished by *Ali.* Within a little while after the *Cadi* came forth to the doore of the Tent, and sayd with a loud voice in the *Turkish, Arabick,* and *Greeke* tongue; That all they who would enter to crave justice, or to lay any other matter against *Ali Bashaw,* might have free entrance: for there was *Hazan Bashaw,* whom the *Grand Signior* hath sent for *Viceroy* of *Cyprus,* who would doe them all right and justice. This license being given, the *Ianizaries* left the doore of the Tent disoccupied, and gave way to such as would enter in; *Mahamut* wrought *Ricardo* to goe in with him, who for that they were *Hazans* slaves, had without any hinderance free accesse thereunto.

There entred to crave justice, some *Greeke-Christians,* and some *Turkes,* but all of them charging him with such trifling things, and of so small moment; that the *Cadi* dispatched most of them, without giving a Copie to the Defendant, without further examination, demaunds, and answers. For all causes, unlesse they be matrimoniall, are dispatched in an instant, more by the judgement of a good understanding man, then the quercks of Law. And amongst these *Barbarians* (if they be so in this particular) the *Cadi* is the competent Iudge of all Causes; who doth abbreviate them, and determine them in the turning of a hand; and forthwith pronounceth sentence without any appealing therefrom, to any other *Tribunall.*

In this interim, entred in a *Chauz,* which is as it were an *Alquazil,* and sayd; That there was a *Iew* at the Tent doore, who had brought to bee sold a most fayre and beautifull *Christian;* the *Cadi* commanded that they should bid him come in: The *Chauz* went forth, and presently came in againe, leading the way to a venerable *Iew,* who led by the hand a Woman in a *Barbarie* habite; so well made and set forth, that the richest *Moore* in *Fez,* or *Morocco,* was not able to compare therewith; for in her whole dresse throughout, she surpassed all the *Affrican* women; yea, though even those of *Argier's* should have presented themselves there with all their Pearles and rich embroyderies. She came in, having her face covered with a scarfe of *Crimson Taffata;* about the smalls of her legges (which discovered themselves) there appeared two golden chaines of pure burnisht gold; and on her armes, which likewise through a smocke of Cendall, or thinne *Taffata-Sarcenet,* were transparant, and shewed themselves to the searching curious eyes of the beholders; she ware two bracelets of gold, wherein were set scatteringly here and there, many fayre Pearles and precious Stones. In conclusion, the fashion of her cloathes, and all other habiliments about her were such, that she presented her selfe before them, most richly and gorgeously attyred.

151

The *Cadi,* and the other two *Bashaw's* upon the very first sight of her, being mightily taken; before any other thing was sayd or questioned by them, they willed the *Iew,* that hee should take the scarfe from off the *Christians* face; Hee did so, and withall did discover such a splendour, and such a beautifull countenance, as did dazle the eyes, and glad the hearts of all the standers by: As the Sunne scarfed with clouds, after much darknesse, offers it selfe to the eyes of those who long for its desired presence; such, and no otherwise then such was the beautie of this Captived *Christian,* in this her braverie and gallantry.

But he, on whom this wonderfull light which was discovered, wrought the greatest and deepest impression, was this our sorrowfull *Ricardo,* as one who better than any other knew her, since that shee was his cruell and beloved *Leonisa,* who so often and with so many teares, had by him been reputed and deplored for dead. With the sodaine and unexpected sight of the singular beautie of this *Christian,* the heart of *Ali* was wounded and captivated; and in the same degree, and with the selfe same wound *Hazan* found himselfe toucht; the *Cadi* himselfe not being exempted from this amorous wound, who more perplexed than both the other, knew not how to remove his eyes from looking on those fayrer lights of *Leonisa.* And for to endeare the great and powerfull force of *Love;* I would have thee to take notice, that at one and the same instant there was bred in the hearts of all these three, one and the same (as they flattered themselves) firme hope of obtaining and enjoying her. And therefore without questioning how, where, and when the *Iew* came by her, they onely asked him what hee would take for her? The covetous *Iew* answered, two thousand Crownes. But hee had scarce set the prise, but that *Ali Bashaw* sayd unto him, that he would give him so much for her; and that hee would goe to his Tent, and presently bring him his money.

But *Hazan Bashaw,* who was minded that he should not have her, though therein he should hazzard his life; sayd, I likewise will give for her those two thousand Crownes which the *Iew* demaundeth; yet would I neither give so much, neither set my selfe to cross *Ali* herein, or what he hath offered, did not that inforce me thereunto; which hee himselfe shall confesse is reason, and doth obliedge and force mee to doe as I doe, and this it is; That this gentile slave appertaineth not to either of us two, but onely to the *Grand-Signior*; and therefore I say, that in his name I buy her: Now let us see who dare bee so bold as to offer to take her from mee.

Marry that dare I, replied *Ali*; because for the selfe same end and purpose doe I buy her: and it appertaineth more especially unto mee, to tender this present to the *Grand-Signior,* in regard of the conveniencie that I have to convey her forthwith to *Constantinople*; carrying her along with me, that thereby I may gaine the good will of the *Grand-Signior.* For I being now a man (as thou now *Hazan* seest) without any charge or command, I had need seek out some meanes to procure it, wherein thou art surely setled for three years, since that this is the very first day in which thou beginnest to beare rule, and to governe this rich king-dome of *Cyprus.* And therefore, as well for these reasons, as that I was the first that offered the propounded prise for her; it stands with all reason (O *Hazan*) that thou leave her unto mee. Nay rather it is more fitting, and will bee better taken at my hands (replied *Hazan*) to pro-cure her and send her to the *Grand Signior*; since that I doe it without being moved thereunto out of mine owne private interest, or ex-pectancie of profit. And whereas you alleadge the commodiousnesse and conveniencie of carrying her along with you; I will set forth a Galley of mine owne well armed, putting thereinto men of mine owne, some servants, some slaves, which shall serve for her Convoy, and goe along with her. At these words *Ali's* bloud began to rise, and rising upon his feet, hee layd his hand on his *Cimyter,* saying; *Hazan,* my intentions being the same, for the presenting and carrying of this *Christian* to the *Grand-Signior,* and I having beene the first chapman that

X

drave the bargaine; it is grounded upon all reason and justice, that
thou leave her unto mee; and if thou shouldst but thinke to carry her
from mee, this *Cimyter* which I lay my hand on shall defend my right,
and chastise thy presumption.

The *Cadi,* who was attentive to all that past betweene them, and
burned no lesse in *Loves* flames then the other two, fearing least hee
might goe without the *Christian;* bethought himselfe how hee might
quench this great fire which was kindled betweene them; and withall,
to get the Captive into his owne custody, without giving any the least
suspicion of his damnable intention. And therefore rising up, he
interposed himselfe betweene them, and said; *Hazan,* and *Ali,* let mee
entreat you both to be quiet, and lay aside these your differences; and
I doubt not but I shall bee able to compose them in such sort, that
both of you may effect your intentions, and the *Grand-Signior* be (as
you desire) well served by you.

To these words of the *Cadi,* they presently shewed themselves
obedient, and had hee commanded them a greater matter, they would
have done it; (so great is the respect which those of that sect beare to
his gray haires.) The *Cadi* then prosecuting what hee had begun in
this manner.

Thou *Ali* sayest, that thou wouldst have this Christian for the
Grand-Signior; and *Hazan* he sayes the like: Thou alleagest, that thou
wast the first in offering the demaunded price for her, and therefore
she ought to bee thine. *Hazan* contradicts thee in this; and though hee
doth not put his argument so home to the pinching point; yet I finde
it is the same as thine is; that is, the same intention, which without all
doubt was hatched as soone as thine was, in his desire and willing-
nesse to buy the Slave for the same effect; onely thou gotst the start of
him, in having first declared thy selfe, yet ought not this to bee a cause
that hee should absolutely and wholy be defrauded and frustrated of
his good desire. And therefore in my opinion, it shall not bee amisse

to accord this businesse betweene you, in this forme and manner following; That both of you shall have equall interreſt in this Slave, and since that the use of her is to bee at the will and pleasure of the *Grand-Signior,* for whom she is bought, it belongeth unto him to dispose of her. In the meane while, you *Hazan* shall pay two thousand Crownes; and *Ali* shall lay downe the other two thousand, and the Captive shall remaine in my power, to the end, that in both your names I may send her to *Conſtantinople,* that neither of you might remaine unrewarded; and can certifie (as being an eye witnesse) your forwardnesse to gratifie the *Grand-Signior*; and therefore offer my selfe to send her thither at my coſt and charge, with that authority and decencie which is due to him, to whom she is sent. Writing to the *Grand-Signior,* acquainting him with all that which passed here, and your readinesse to do him this service.

These two enamoured *Turkes,* neither knew, nor could, nor would contradict him; each of them forming and imagining in his minde a hope (though doubtfull) of promising to themselves the attaining to the end of their inflamed desires. *Hazan,* who was to continue *Viceroy* of *Cyprus,* thought upon giving great gifts to the *Cadi,* that being thereby overcome and obliged, he should deliver up unto him the Captive. And *Ali* he imagined to do some such act as should assure the obtaining of what he desired, and each of them holding his owne designe the beſt, and the sureſt; they easily condiscended to what the *Cadi* had propounded, and with a joynt consent both of them delivered her up presently unto him, and made each of them present payment to the *Iew* 1000 Crownes a peece: But the *Iew* sayd hee would not part with her upon those tearmes, if they meant to have into the bargaine her wearing apparrell, and her jewels, which hee valewed at 1000 Crownes more. And in very deed they could be little lesse worth, because in her haires which partly hung dishevell'd on her shoulders, and partly knit up in curious knots on her fore-head, there appeared some ropes of pearles, which very gracefully were interwoven with them. The bracelet about her armes, and above her ancles in the small of the legge were likewise full of great pearles; her rayment throughout was very rich, and theron a mantle after the Moorish manner of greene Sattin deepely fringed and embroydered with gold.

In a word, it seemed to all that were there present, that the *Iew* had undervalued the at-tyring of her. And the *Cadi,* that hee might not shew himselfe lesse liberall then the two *Bashaw's,* told him, hee would pay him those thousand Crownes, because hee would have her to be presented in the same dresse (which she was now in) to the *Grand-Signior.* The two competitors did approve very well of it, each of them beleeving that all should fall out as they would have it.

I want now words significant enough to tell you what *Ricardo* thought, in seeing his soule set out thus to open sale; and those thoughts which then came into his head, and those feares which sodainely surprized him; when as he saw that his finding of his beloved Pledge was to lose her the more; He knew not for a while, whether he were sleeping or waking, not beleeving his owne eyes, in giving credit to that which they had seene. For it seemed unto him a thing impossible, that they should see so unexpectedly before them, those eyes of hers which hee had (not long since) given to bee shut up in eternall darkenesse.

When hee saw that this was no phantasma or dreame, but a reall truth; hee came to his friendly *Mahamut,* and whispering him in the eare, sayd softly unto him; Friend, dost not thou know her? Not I sayd *Mahamut*; Then would I have thee know, (replied *Ricardo*) that it is *Leonisa*: How (answered *Mahamut*) what is that *Ricardo*, thou sayest? That (sayd *Ricardo*) which thou hast already heard. Hold thy peace then, and doe not discover her, replied *Mahamut*, for *Fortune* goes now so ordering the businesse, that thou shalt finde her good and prosperous, since that shee is in my Masters power. Dost thou thinke it fit, sayd *Ricardo*, that I goe and put my selfe in some such place where I may bee seene by her? No, by no meanes, replied *Mahamut*; least shee should put you, or you her into some sodaine passion; and have a great care that you doe not give any the least signe or token that you know her, or that ever you had seen her; for if you should do so, it might redound much to the prejudice of my designe, if not utterly overthrow it. I will follow your advise, answered *Ricardo*, and so went his way, leaving the place, least his eyes might encounter with those of *Leonisa*; who held hers all the while that this passed nayled to the ground, trilling some teares downe from them.

Shee being thus (as you have heard) rendred up unto the *Cadi*, he came unto her, and laying hands on her, delivered her unto *Mahamut*, commanding him to carry her to the Citie, with charge to deliver her to his Lady *Halima*; and to tell her withall, that she should use and intreat her well, as being the slave of the *Grand-Signior*. *Mahamut* did so, and left *Ricardo* all alone, who with his eyes went following this his Star, till it was wholy taken out of his sight, and covered as it were with a cloud from him by the walls of *Nicosia*. Having lost her, hee goes to looke out the *Iew*, findes him; and comming civilly unto him, askt him where he had bought this Captive *Christian*, and how, and in what manner shee came into his hand. The *Iew* made him answer, that hee lighted on her in the Island of *Pantanalea*; and that he bought her of certaine *Turkes*, whose Galley had suffered wrack, being split there against the Rocks. And being willing to have gone on in the prosecution of what hee had begun, it received interruption, and was wholy broken off by one that came from the *Bashaw's*, telling the *Iew* that he must come away presently unto them who had purposely sent for him; that they might demand that of him, which *Ricardo* was so desirous to know, and thereupon he abruptly tooke his leave.

In the way, which was betweene the Tents and the Towne, *Mahamut* tooke occasion to aske *Leonisa* (speaking unto her in *Italian*) whence shee was, and of what place? Who made him answer, that shee was of the Citie of *Trapana*: Then *Mahamut* demanded againe of her, whether she did know in that Citie, a rich and noble Gentleman, called *Ricardo*? At her hearing him named, *Leonisa* fetcht a deepe sighe, saying; Too too well to my hurt. How, to your hurt? replied *Mahamut*. Because hee knew me (sayd *Leonisa*) to his owne, and my unhappinesse. But I pray tell mee (quoth *Mahamut*) Did you know likewise in the sayd Citie another Gentleman of a gentile disposition, the Sonne of very rich Parents, and himselfe in his owne person very valiant, very liberall, and very discreet, called *Cornelio*? I likewise know him (sayd *Leonisa*) and I may say much more to my hurt than *Ricardo*.

But I pray Sir who are you, who know these two, and aske mee of them? I am (sayd *Mahamut*) of *Palermo,* and by various accidents in this disguise and different habite from that which I was wont to weare. I know them passing well, for it is not many dayes since that they were both in my power. For certaine *Moores* of *Tripoli* in *Barbarie* had taken *Cornelio* Captive, and sold him to a *Turke,* who brought him to this Island, whether he came with Merchandize, (for hee is a Merchant of *Rhodes*) who had trusted *Cornelio* with all his goods. And hee will keepe them well, (sayd *Leonisa*) because he knows so well to keepe his own.

But tell mee Sir, how, or with whom *Ricardo* came to this Island? Marry hee came (answered *Mahamut*) with a Pyrate who tooke him prisoner in a Garden neare the sea-shoare of *Trapana*; and that together with him, hee had Captivated a Damosell, but I could never get him to tell me her name. He abode here some few daies with his Master, who was to goe to visit *Mahomets* Sepulchre, which is in the Citie of *Almedina*: But just at the time of his departure, *Ricardo* fell so extreame sicke, that his Master left him with me (for that I was his Countrey-man,) to the end, that I might use all the best meanes for his recoverie, and take care and charge of him, till his returne; and in case that hee did not returne hither, that I should send him unto him to *Constantinople*, whereof he would advertise me when he came thither.

But Heaven had otherwise ordered it, since that unfortunate *Ricardo* without having any accident or simptome of a dangerous sicknesse, within a few dayes ended those of his life; making often mention of one *Leonisa*, whom (as himselfe told me) hee loved more then his owne life, and was as deare unto him, if not dearer then his owne soule. Which *Leonisa* (as he at large related unto mee) suffered ship-wrack at the Island of *Pantanalea*, the Galley wherein shee was, being split upon the Rockes, and her selfe drowned, Whose death hee con-tinually lamented, and with much weeping bewayled, till that his mourning had brought him to breath his last; for I perceived no sicknesse at all in him in his bodie, but great shewes of griefe and sorrow in his soule.

Tell mee (Sir) replied *Leonisa*; this other young man whom you speake off, in those his discourses which hee had with you; which (for that you were of his owne Countrey) could not but be very many, did he not at any time speake of *Leonisa*? And did he tell you, how shee, and *Ricardo* were made Captives, and the whole manner of it? Speake of her (sayd *Mahamut*) yes a thousand, and a thousand times; and asked mee many a time and oft, whether any Christian of this name had of late beene brought to this Island, and with such and such markes and tokens, and how glad hee would bee to heare any tydings of her, that he might ransome her. And withall I must tell you, that hee had told his Master, and in telling, made him beleeve that shee was not so rich as he tooke her to bee; and for that he had enjoyed her, he might now make the lesse reckoning of her; and that if three or foure hundred Crowns would purchase her freedome, he would willingly give so much for her, because heretofore he had borne some good will and affection towards her.

Very little (sayd *Leonisa*) must that his affection be, which would not goe beyond foure hundred Crownes. But *Ricardo* is more liberall, more valiant, more generous, and ingenious, then to make so poore an offer, for that which hee prized at so high a valew. God pardon the party that was the cause of his death; for it was I that am that unhappy woman whom hee bewayled for dead; and God knowes, if I should not bee glad with all my heart that hee were alive, that I might requite his kindnesse, and that hee might see how sensible I should be of his misfortune, who hath sorrowed so much for mine.

I Sir (as I have already told you) am shee, who is as little beloved of *Cornelio,* as I was greatly bewayled of *Ricardo*; She, who by very many and various chances am come to this miserable estate wherin I now find my self; and though it bee so dangerous (as you see) yet have I alwaies by Heavens gracious assistance, kept mine honour entire and untoucht, wherewith in this my misery I live contented. But now (woe is mee) neither doe I know where I am, nor who is my Master, nor whether my contrarious fates will hurrie mee. Wherefore I beseech you Sir, by that bloud which you have in you of a Christian, that you will give mee your best counsaile and advise in these my troubles; which for that they have beene many, though they have made mee looke about and bee somewhat the more warie and circum⁄spect; yet notwithstanding, such and so many every moment came upon mee, that I knew not well how to prevent and withstand them.

Whereunto *Mahamut* answered, that he would doe all whatsoever he was able to doe, in serving, advising, and assisting her with his best wit and strength. And then did hee advertise her of the difference betweene the two *Bashaw's* for her sake, and how that she now remained in the power of the *Cadi* his Master, for the conveying and presenting her to the great *Turke, Selim,* at *Constantinople.* But rather then this should take effect, he hoped in the true God, in whom hee beleeved, (though a bad Christian) that he would dispose otherwise of her; advising her withall, that by bearing her selfe fayrely, she should work and insinuate her selfe into *Halima's* favour and good opinion, Wife to the *Cadi* his Master, in whose power she was to remaine till they should send her to *Constantinople*; acquainting her withall, with *Halima's* conditions and qualities; and besides these, told her many other things which might make much for her good, holding talke and discourse with her all the way, till he had brought her to, and left her in the *Cadi's* house, and in the power of *Halima,* to whom hee delivered his Masters message. The *Moore,* for that she saw she was so well clad, and so beautifull, gave her a very kinde and friendly welcome. *Mahamut* having rendred up his charge into *Halima's* hands, returned back to the Tents, to recount unto *Ricardo* what had passed betwixt himselfe, and *Leonisa*; and meeting with him, told him all, point by point, from the beginning to the ending. But when I came to tell him how sorrowfull *Leonisa* was, when I signified unto her, that hee was dead, the water stood in his eyes: I told him how I had feigned that counterfeit story of *Cornelio's* being a Captive, to see how she would take it; I acquainted him with her coldnesse to *Cornelio,* and the bad conceit she had of him for his undervaluing her. All which was as a soveraigne cordiall to *Ricardo's* afflicted heart; Who sayd unto *Mahamut.*

There comes now into my minde (friend *Mahamut*) a tale which my Father told mee, who (you know) how curious hee was; and have heard (I am sure) what great honour the Emperour *Charles* the Fifth

did him, whom he still serv'd in honourable places in his Warres:
I tell you that he told me, that when the Emperour was at the Siege
of *Tunez* and tooke it, together with the Fort *Goleta*; being one day
in the field in his Tent, they presented unto him a *Moore,* as a singular

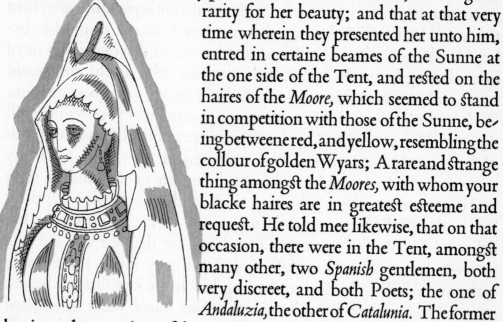

rarity for her beauty; and that at that very
time wherein they presented her unto him,
entred in certaine beames of the Sunne at
the one side of the Tent, and rested on the
haires of the *Moore,* which seemed to stand
in competition with those of the Sunne, being betweene red, and yellow, resembling the
collour of golden Wyars; A rare and strange
thing amongst the *Moores,* with whom your
blacke haires are in greatest esteeme and
request. He told mee likewise, that on that
occasion, there were in the Tent, amongst
many other, two *Spanish* gentlemen, both
very discreet, and both Poets; the one of
Andaluzia, the other of *Catalunia.* The former
having taken a view of her, vented certaine verses, which they call
Coplas, ending in rhime; but being at a stand when hee had uttered
five of his verses; the other gentleman (seeing him sticke, and that hee
could goe no further to make an end of what hee had begunne, for
want of words which on the suddaine did not offer themselves to his
liking,) who stood close by him, and had heard these his Verses, went
presently on where hee left, adding instantly five other to the former.
And this presented it selfe unto my memorie, when I saw that most
beautifull *Leonisa* enter the *Bashaw's* Tent; not onely out shining the
beames of the Sunne, should they have lighted on her, but even Heaven
it selfe, with all it's starres.

Hold (sayd *Mahamut*) no more, least (friend *Ricardo*) thy tongue

runne riot, for at every word thou utterest, I am afrayd thou wilt passe
so farre beyond the bounds, of not onely reason, but religion, in the
praise and commendation of thy fayre *Leonisa*, that leaving to seeme
a Christian, thou wilt bee taken for a Gentile. Let mee heare those
verses or *Coplas*, or what else you please to call them, that wee may
afterwards talke of other things that may bee more pleasing, and perhaps more profitable. In good time (sayd *Ricardo*) but let mee once
againe advertise thee that the *Andaluz* vented the first five verses, and
the *Catalan* the other five, both *ex tempore,* and these they bee.

And. „ *Whilest I behold thy glittering golden hayres,*
  „ *Disheveld thus, waving about thy eares,*
  „ *And see those lockes thus loosed and undone,*
  „ *For their more pompe to sport them in the Sunne,*
  „ *Love takes those threads, and weaves them with that Art,*
Cat. „ *Hee knits a thousand knots about my heart,*
  „ *And with such skill and cunning bee them sets,*
  „ *My soule lies taken in those lovely nets.*
  „ *Making mee cry, faire prison that dost hold*
  „ *My heart in fetters wrought of burnisht gold.*

I like them well (sayd *Mahamut*) but much better (my *Ricardo*) that
you are in this good humour of repeating verses, because the saying or
making of them requireth the mindes of men that are disapassionated.
Men likewise use (replyed *Ricardo*) to wayle over Hearses, as to sing
verses, both are verse.

But laying this aside, tell mee what thou mindest to do in this our
businesse? for though I understood not what the *Bashaw's* treated in
the Tent, till thou hast carried away *Leonisa*; a *Renegado* of my Master
a *Venetian* told me all, who was then present, and understood the
Turkish language very well. And therefore above all things it is
most needfull and requisite to set our wits a worke, and seeke out

some plot to prevent *Leonisa's* comming to the hands of the *Grand Signior.*

That which is fittest first of all to bee done (answered *Mahamut*) is, that thou come to bee in the power of my Master. This being effected, wee will afterwards consult on that which shall convene best for us. Whilest they were thus talking, came the Guardian of the Christian Captives belonging to *Hazan,* and carried *Ricardo* away with him.

The *Cadi* returned with *Hazan* to the Citie, who in a few dayes dispatched *Ali's* Residencie, and gave it him roll'd up and sealed, that hee might carry it along with him to *Constantinople.* Hee taking his leave, prepared forthwith to set forward on his journey, being very instant with the *Cadi,* that hee would hasten the sending of the Captive, and withall write his Letters to the *Grand Signior* in his favour, for the better furthering of his pretensions: the *Cadi* promised him he would, but with trecherous bowells which were almost turned into ashes, so were they set on fire by the inflamed love which he bare to the Captive.

Ali being gone full of false hopes, and *Hazan* abiding behinde not voyd of them; *Mahamut* so brought the businesse about, that *Ricardo* came into the power of his Master. Houres and dayes ran on, the time past away and the longing desire to see *Leonisa,* did so presse and wring *Ricardo,* that hee could not take one poore short minute of rest.

Ricardo changed his owne name into that of *Mario,* because his might not come to *Leonisa's* eares, before that his eyes had seene her. And for to see her was very hard and difficult; for that the *Moores* are extreamly jealous, and keep covered from all men the faces of their women; howbeit they doe not much mislike the shewing of them to Christians, which happily may bee; because being Captives, they doe not reckon them for men, but slight them as contemptible creatures.

Yet one day it so happened, that the Lady *Halima* saw her slave *Mario*; and in seeing him, tooke such a good liking of him, that hee remained deepely engraven in her heart, and ſtrongly fixed in her memory. And peradventure taking little contentment in the cold and weake embracements of her aged husband, she the more easily gave way to this her evill desire. And with the like easinesse shee ac-quainted *Leonisa* therewith, whom she now dearely loved, and made exceeding much of, for her sweete behaviour, and discreet carriage; and likewise shewed her great respeſt, for that shee was to be sent for a raritie to the *Grand-Signior*. She acquainted her, how that the *Cadi* had brought and received into his house a *Chriſtian* Captive, of so gentle an aspeſt, and comely presence; that in her eye, he was the handsomeſt man that ever shee saw in her life: and that they sayd he was a *Chilibi,* that is to say a Gentleman, and Countrey-man to *Mahamut,* their *Renegado*; and that shee knew not how to give him clearely to underſtand the good will and affeſtion which she bare unto him; fearing leaſt that the *Chriſtian* should slight and negleſt her, for declaring and manifeſting her love unto him at the firſt sight, before she had further and better knowledge of him.

Leonisa askt her what was the Captives name: *Halima* told her *Mario*: to whom *Leonisa* replied; if he be a Gentleman, and of that place they say he is, certainely I should know him; but of this name (*Mario,*) I doe not remember that there is any such in *Trapana*. But if it shall ſtand with your Ladiships pleasure that I may but see him, and talke a while with him, I shall be able to informe you both who he is, and what may be hoped from him; It shall be so sayd *Halima,* and on Friday next, when as the *Cadi* shall bee at the *Mezquita,* performing those Rites and Ceremonies which are then and there required in their devotions, and adorations; I will take occasion to call him in hither, where leaving you two together, you may talke alone by your selves; and if you thinke fit, you may give him some inckling of my desires, and well wishings towards him, and that you will doe me this friendly office in the beſt manner your wit and discretion can devise, of both which I have had already sufficient tryall, and therefore need not to expresse my selfe, or presse you any farther in this particular.

This *Halima* sayd to *Leonisa*, and within lesse then two houres after, the *Cadi* called *Mahamut*, and *Mario* unto him, and with no lesse effecacie then *Halima* had discovered her heart to *Leonisa*, did this enamoured old young man discover his to his two slaves, craving their councell and advise, what course he should take for to keepe the *Christian* to himselfe, and enjoy her; and yet cumply with the *Grand Signior* whose she was: telling them withall, that hee would rather dye a thousand deaths, then deliver her up once to the great *Turke*.

With such affection did this *Moore* expresse his passions, that they left a deepe impression and beliefe in the hearts of his two slaves; whose thoughts were fully bent to runne a contrary course to that which he imagined. He thought one thing, and they another; in the end, it was concluded betweene them, that *Mario,* as being a man of her owne Nation and Countrey (howbeit he had told him that hee knew her not) should take in hand the soliciting her, and in declaring his fervent affection: And in case that by his faire meanes hee could not prevaile and procure her good will, he should then use force, she being now in his power: and this being done, to give out that she was dead, and so hee should excuse his sending of her to *Constantinople*.

The *Cadi* rested wonderfull well contented with this devise of his slaves, and out of the great joy which he had imagined to himselfe, he instantly gave *Mahamut* his libertie; bequeathing besides unto him after his death, the one halfe of his goods. Hee likewise promised *Mario,* if he procured that which hee so earnestly desired, not onely his libertie, but good store of Crownes, wherewith he should returne home to his owne Countrey, rich, honoured, and contented.

If he were liberall in promising, his Captives were prodigall, offering to hale downe the Moone from Heaven, to doe him service, how much more easily to draw *Leonisa* to the bent of his Bow, and to condiscend to his desire; so as *Mario* by his leave might have the conveniencie offered him of speaking with her. I will give him free leave of accesse unto her, answered the *Cadi*, even as often as hee will himselfe, if that will advance the businesse. For I will so order it, that *Halima* shall goe hence to the house of her Parents, who are *Greeke-Christians*, where shee shall stay some few daies, or longer time (if need be;) and she being abroad, I will command my Porter that he suffer *Mario* to enter into the house, and to have free ingresse and egresse, as oft as he pleaseth. And I will tell *Leonisa*, that she may (if it please her) talke and converse with her Countrey-man.

Thus did the winde begin to chop about of *Ricardo's* misfortunes, blowing with a gentle gale in his favour, his Master not witting which way hee meant to shape his course. This appointment being made and concluded on between these three; the first that laid this plott was *Halima*, shewing her self a right woman, whose nature is facile, and whose wit quicke, and sodaine, for the effecting of that which she hath a minde unto; especially if her heart bee eagerly set upon it. That very selfe same day, the *Cadi* came to *Halima*, and told her, that shee might when she would goe out of the Towne to visit her Father and Mother, and make merry with them, and the rest of her good friends; and to stay there as long as she listed, or till hee sent for her. But because her heart was over-joyed with those good hopes which *Leonisa* had given her; shee not onely would not go to her Parents house, nor yet to that feigned Paradise of *Mahomet*: and therefore told him, that at this time she had no great minde to goe thither, When she had, she would acquaint him therewith; but whensoever she went, she would carry the Captive *Christian* along with her. O by no meanes (replyed the *Cadi*,) for it is not fit, that this Pledge of the *Grand-Signior* should bee seene of any; besides, it would do her more hurt than good to converse with *Christians*, since that you know, that when she comes into the power of the *Grand-Signior*, she must be shut up in the *Seraglio*, and turne *Turke* whether she will or no. But if she go along with me, replyed *Halima,* it mattereth not much that she be in my Parents house, nor that she converse with them, with whom my selfe converse much more, and yet I cease not for all that to bee a good *Turke.* Besides, the longest time that I meane to spend with them in their house, shall be at the farthest, but foure or five dayes; for the great love which I beare unto you, will not give me leave to be any longer absent, and not see you. The *Cadi* made no reply, that hee might not give her occasion to breed some suspition or other in her, of his intention.

Whilest this businesse was a brewing, Friday came, and he went to the *Mezquita,* from whence he could not come forth in almost foure houres; and *Halima* had scarce seene him put his foot over the threshold of his house, but shee commanded *Mario* to be call'd for to come unto her; but a *Christian* of *Corsica* would not suffer him to enter, who was then Porter and wayted at the gate of the outward Court; if *Halima* her selfe had not called out aloud unto him that hee should let him come in. And so hee entred, but much troubled, and trembling, as if hee had beene to fight with a whole armie of enemies.

Leonisa was in the same dresse and attyre as when shee entred the *Bashaw's* Tent, sitting at the foot of a curious stayr-case of polished Marble, which led the way up to a large and spacious gallerie round-ing the whole house; her head hung downeward towards her bosome, resting it selfe on the palme of her right hand, and leaning her elbow on her knee, her eyes were turned another way quite contrarie to the doore by which *Mario* entred; so that though hee went towards the place where shee sate, yet did she not see him.

No sooner was *Ricardo* let in, but hee walked through the whole house with his eyes, yet could he not perceive any thing save a dumbe and still silence, till that hee cast his eye aside where *Leonisa* sate: Instantly whereupon, so many thoughts tooke hold on enamoured *Ricardo,* as did worke in him both amazement and gladnesse, conceiting himselfe to bee a thousand paces and more distanced from his happinesse and contentment. Hee considered likewise with himselfe that hee was a Captive, and his glorie in anothers power: revolving these things with himselfe, he made towards her by a little and a little, and with a fearefull love, a joyfull sadnesse, and timerous courage, (for such passions accompanie true lovers) hee came by degrees to the Center where his hearts joy was, when by chance *Leonisa* turned her head aside, and fixed her eyes on those of *Mario,* who looked very stedfastly on her.

But when both their lookes had thus encountred each other, by different effects gave evident signes of that which their severall soules felt within. *Ricardo* stood stock still and could not stirre one foot further; and *Leonisa,* who upon *Mahamuts* relation gave *Ricardo* for dead, and to see him now and that so unexpectedly alive, full of feare, and amazement, without unfixing her eyes, or turning her backe, shee stept up backeward foure or five stayres, she blest her selfe as if shee had seene some phantasma, or a thing of another World.

Ricardo returned from out his astonishment, and knew by that which *Leonisa* did, the true cause of her feare, and therefore sayd unto her; it grieves mee to the very soule, (oh of all fayre, the fayrest *Leonisa*) that the newes did not fall out true which *Mahamut* gave thee of my death, for by it I might have excused those feares which now I have, in thinking with my selfe whether that rigour which heretofore thou hast used towards me, continue still in the same force and being? Quiet your selfe (dearest in my love) and come downe againe, and if you dare do that which hitherto you never did, which is; to draw neare unto me, come and touch me, and thou shalt see that I am no phantasticall bodie, no wandring ghost; I am *Ricardo* (*Leonisa*) that unfortunate *Ricardo* whom thou hast made so.

Whilest he was speaking this, *Leonisa* puts her finger upon her mouth, whereby *Ricardo* understood that it was a signe that hee should be silent, or speake more softly: and taking a little better heart unto him, he drew a little nearer unto her in such a distance, that he might heare these words come from her. Speake lower (*Mario*) for so me thinketh thou now callest thy selfe, and treate not of any other thing now, save what I shall treate with thee; and consider withall that it may so happen that if we be over heard, we shall never see one another any more: I verily beleeve that *Halima* our Mistresse listeneth to heare, if not heareth us; who (to deale plainely and briefly with thee) hath told me that she adores thee, and hath entreated me to be the inter- cessoresse of this her desire: if thou wilt answer her wishes, it will bee better for thy bodie then thy soule. But if thou wilt not, yet must thou feigne that thou dost embrace her love; as well because I entreate thee so to do, as also for that the declared desires of a Woman ought not uncivily to be despised and utterly rejected.

Hereunto *Ricardo* answered, I did never thinke nor ever could imagine (fayrest *Leonisa*) that there was that thing whatsoever which you should entreate me to doe, that should bring with it an impossi- bilitie of cumplying therewith: but that which you now require of mee, hath dis-deceived me: Is peradventure mans will so light, that it may be moved too and fro, and carried hither and thither, whether the pleasure of others shall guide and direct it? or doth it stand with the honour and faith of a Gentleman, or with the repute of an honest man, to feigne and dissemble in things of such weight and high a nature as this is? If it seeme good unto you, that any of these things in this kinde ought to bee or may be done; doe that which shall be most pleasing in your owne eyes, because you are the sole Mistresse of my will. But I now know that you likewise deceive me in this, since that you never rightly knew my will, and therefore know not how to dispose thereof; but because you may not say that in the first thing you commanded me, you should not bee obeyed; I will lose somewhat of my selfe, and of being what I ought to be, I will satisfie your desire, and that if *Halima* (as you say) feignedly, so that I may thereby gaine the happines to see you. And therefore doe you feigne my answers to your owne good liking, for from hence forth my feigned will doth firme, and confirme them. Now in requitall of this office which I do for you, which is in my opinion the greatest that ever I can or shall be able to doe, though I should give my soule anew unto you, which I have so often given you; I beseech you, that you will briefly tell me, how you escaped from the hands of the Pirats, and how you came to those of the *Iew*, who so lately sold you.

The storie of my misfortunes (answered *Leonisa*) require more leisure then time will now permit to relate, yet notwithstanding I will not leave you wholy unsatisfied. Know then, that the same very evening we parted, *Yzuph's* Galley was with a stiffe and strong winde driven to the same Isles of *Pantanalea*, where wee likewise saw your Vessell; but ours, wee being not able to hinder it, ranne remedilesly upon the Rockes. My Master then having his destruction before his eyes, and that there was little or no hope of safety left; with all possible haste emptied two Hogsheads which were full of water, then stopped up the bung-holes very close, and having bound the one to the other with good strong cords, he seated me betweene them; that done hee presently stript himselfe, and taking another Hogshead, spreading his armes over it, and binding a rope about his middle, causing the same to bee fastned to the Caskes whereon I sate bound, with great courage hee rushed into the Sea, towing mee after him. I had not the heart to rush in after him, which one of the Turkes seeing, pushed mee forward with all his force, and sent mee packing after *Yzuph,* where I lay without any sense, nor came againe to my selfe, till I found my selfe on

Land in the armes of two Turkes; who bowing my head and bodie towards the ground, held me so a pretty space, all that while great store of salt-water which I had swallowed downe, comming forth at my mouth.

At last I opened mine eyes, but as one amazed, and looking about, who should I see, but *Yzuph* lying by me with his braines beaten out against the Rockes when hee had almost recovered the shoare, where hee ended his life. This I afterwards understood by the Turkes; and they likewise told mee, that taking hold of the Cord, they drew mee on Land, without receiving any further harme then what I mentioned before unto you; of all the whole companie, onely eight persons escaped drowning. Eight daies wee abode in the Island, the Turkes using mee with as much respect as if I had beene their Sister, if not more. Wee kept our selves close in a Cave, the Turkes fearing that if they should bee espied, the Christians which had the command of the Fort which is in the Island, would salley forth upon them and take them Captive. They sustained themselves with wet bisket which the Sea had cast upon the shoare from out the broken bins of the Galley, which they went forth to gather up by night that they might not be discovered.

Fortune had so ordered it for my great ill, that the Fort was without a Captaine, who died but a few daies before, and in all the Fort there were not above twenty souldiers. This we came to know by a youth which was captivated by the Turkes, who came downe from thence to gather Cockles by the Sea-side. At the eight daies end, there arrived on that Coast a Vessell of the *Moores,* which they call *Cara-mucales;* the Turkes saw it's comming in, and that they lay at Anchor a little off the Land and so made towards them, making such signes to the Vessell which was not far off, that they who were in her knew they were Turkes that called unto them. Thereupon they sent out their Cock-boat, and they recounted upon them their distresse, and they received them into their Barque wherein came an exceeding rich Iew, a Merchant; and all the lading of the Vessell, or the most part of it was his, being fraughted with Carpets, and Hides, and other commodities which they bring from *Barbary*, to the *Levant*. In the said Vessell the Turkes went for *Tripoli*, and in that Voyage they sold me to the *Iew* for two thousand Duckats, an excessive prise, if his love towards me had not made him so liberall, which the *Iew* afterwards discovered unto me.

Leaving the Turkes after all this in *Tripoli*, the Vessell tackt about to performe her Voyage, and the *Iew* in most impudent manner fell to soliciting of mee; but I shewed him such a countenance as his filthy desires deserved. Seing himselfe then in despaire of obtaining his lustfull ends, he resolved to rid himselfe of me upon the first occasion that should offer it selfe unto him. And it comming to his knowledge that the two *Bashaw's, Ali,* and *Hazan* were in this Island, where he might sell and vent his Merchandize as well as in *Xio* whither he was bound; he came hither with intention to sell me to one of the two *Bashaw's*; and for this cause put mee into this dresse and weare wherein you now see me, for to affectionate them the more unto me who should buy me.

I am given to understand that this *Cadi* hath bought me, with purpose to carry me for a Present to the *Great-Turke*, whereof I am not a little afraid. Here I came to know thy feigned death; and I must now tell thee if thou wilt believe me, and believe me thou maist, that it grieved me to the very soule, and that I did more envie then pittie thee; yet not out of any ill will that I bare unto thee, though I did not answer thy love according to thy expectation, (for I shall never be ingratefull and dis-respective, where I have found so much love and respect) but because thou hadst then made an end of thy lives Tragedie.

Deare *Leonisa*, answered *Ricardo*, you say not amisse herein; if death had not hindered the happines of my comming againe to see you, esteeming more this instant of glorie which I enjoy in seeing you; then any other happinesse (saving that which is eternall) which either in life, or in death, might assure unto me my desire.

The *Cadi* now my Master, into whose power I am come, by no lesse various accidents then yours, beares the like fervent affection unto you, as *Halima* doth to me; hee hath made choice of mee to bee the interpreter of his thoughts. I entertained the motion, not for to doe him any pleasure thereby, but that I might gaine the commoditie and conveniencie of speaking with you; to the end that you may see (*Leonisa*) to what hard termes our misfortunes have brought us; you to be the meanes of working an impossibilitie (for you know my minde touching the motion you made unto mee) and me to be likewise set a worke about such a businesse as I least dream't of, and for which I would give, rather then obtaine it, my life which now I esteeme according to it's high worth and valew, since that it hath had the happinesse to see you.

I know not what to say unto thee *Ricardo*, replied *Leonisa,* nor how we shall be able to get out of this intricate laborinth, whereinto (as thou sayest) our hard fortune hath brought us; onely I know to say thus much, that we must be driven in this businesse to use that which is contrary to our condition, and hatefull to honest mindes; to wit, dissembling, and deceit. And therefore say unto thee, that I will acquaint *Halima* with some such words delivered by thee, that shall rather entertaine her with hopes, then drive her to dispaire. Thou like-wise shalt say of me to the *Cadi* that which thou shalt thinke most convenient for the securing of mine honour, and the deceiving of him. And since that I put mine honour into thy hands, thou maist assure thy selfe that it is yet as true and entire as ever; though the many wayes which I have gone, and the many assaults which I have endured might call it into question, though you nor any else without great injustice, can make the least doubt of it. For our speaking and conversing each with other, will be (by their meanes) most facile and easie: always presupposed, that you never once open your mouth, nor treate ought with me, which shall any way appertaine to your declared pretension; for in what houre you shall doe that, in the same you shall take your leave of seeing mee any more. For I would not have thee thinke that my valew is of so little worth, and of so few qualities, that Captivity shall worke that with me, which liberty could not do. I will be (by heavens favour) like gold, which the longer it is in the Chrysoll, comes forth thence the purer, and the finer: rest satisfied and content thy selfe with that which I have alreadie said unto thee, least the very sight of thee should (as it hath done heretofore) cause a distance in me, if not a loathing. For I would have thee to know (*Ricardo*) that I alwaies held thee to be too rough and arrogant, and to presume somewhat more of thy selfe then was fitting. I confesse like-wise that I may be deceived; and it may be that making this tryall of thee, experience will set the truth before mine eyes, and tell mee I was deceived; and being put out of this errour, I may bee more kinde, but never lesse honest: goe get you gone, for I feare me *Halima* may have over-heard us, who hath some understanding of our Christian lan-guage; at least of that mingled speech which is used, whereby wee all understand one another.

You say very well (Mistris of my heart) answered *Ricardo*, and I in-finitely thanke you, and take in exceeding good part this dis-deceiving which you have given mee; and make as high esteeme thereof, as of the favour you doe mee in suffering me to see you. And as you say experience peradventure will make knowne unto you how plaine and downe-right my condition is, and how meek and humble my disposition, especially for to adore you; and had you not put a bound and limit to my carriage and treating with you, yet should it have beene so fayre and so honest towards you, as you cannot wish or desire to have it better.

Touching that which concerneth the entertaining of the *Cadi,* take you no care of that, leave it to me, doe you the like with *Halima*. And by the way, I would have you (Lady) to know, that since I have seene you, there is bred in me such a strong hope and confidence; as assureth mee that it shall not bee long before wee procure our desired libertie, and so God have you in his keeping; at another time, and better leisure, I shall relate unto you the revolutions, the turnings and wind⁄ings by which fortune hath brought me to this estate, after that she had put us asunder and sever'd me from your sight: with this they tooke their leaves each of other, *Leonisa* remaining well contented and satisfied with *Ricardo's* plaine proceeding, and he the most joyfull man in the world, that he had heard one word from *Leonisa's* mouth without tartnesse.

Halima had shut up her selfe in her oratorie, praying to her prophet *Mahomet,* that *Leonisa* might bring her a good dispatch of that businesse which she had recommended unto her. The *Cadi,* he was in the *Mezquita,* recompensing with his desires those of his wife, they keeping him very solicitous, as wholy depending on the answer which hee hoped to heare from his Slave, to whose charge hee had committed his talking with *Leonisa*; and that hee might better come to have some speech with her, *Mahamut* should afford him opportunitie, though that *Halima* were in the house.

Leonisa encreased in *Halima* her lewd lust and filthie desire, by giving her very good hopes that *Mario* would condiscend to her will, and doe whatsoever shee would command him. But telling her withall, that shee must have patience till two Moones were first past over; before which time hee could not cumply with that which hee much more desired then her selfe. And this terme hee entreated of her, that hee might make his prayers and supplications unto God, for the freeing of him from his Captivitie, and restoring him againe to his former libertie. *Halima* contented her selfe with the excuse and relation of her beloved *Ricardo,* whom she would free from his slaverie, before the deputed time, so as hee would accomplish her desire. And there⁄

fore entreated *Leonisa,* that shee would treate with him, and see if shee could worke him to dispence with the sayd time, and to cut off all delaies; and she would furnish him with as much money as the *Cadi* should require of him for his ransome.

Now before that *Ricardo* returned an answer to his Master, he consulted with *Mahamut* what answer hee should make him; and they agreed betweene them to tell him, that the case was desperate, no hope of winning her, and that as soone as possibly he could, he should carry her away to *Constantinople*; and that in the way thitherward, either by faire meanes, or by force obtaine his desire. And as touching the inconvenience which might offer it selfe for his cumplying with the *Grand-Signior,* hee should doe well to buy him another Slave; and in the voyage to feign and cause it to be given out that *Leonisa* was fallen sicke, and making our advantage of a darke night, we may cast the bought Christian over-boord into the Sea, saying; that it was *Leonisa,* the Captive of the *Grand-Signior* that was dead: and that may be done, and should be done in such manner that the truth thereof should never be discovered, and so remaine blamelesse with the *Grand-Signior,* and fulfill his owne will; and that for the continuation of his pleasure, they would afterwards devise some convenient course, that should make all safe and sure.

This poore man, this old *Cadi,* his love to *Leonisa* made him so blinde, that had they told him a thousand other greater unlikelihoods (so as they were directed to the fulfilling of his hopes) he would have believed them all; how much more when it seemed unto him, that all which they said, was good and currant, and in a very faire way, promising prosperous successe. And so indeed it might have proved, if the intention of these his two counsellors had not beene to make themselves Masters of the Vessell, and to make an end of him, and his foolish thoughts together.

But another difficultie offered it selfe to the *Cadi,* which in his owne

A a

opinion was greater then all the rest, it running still in his head that his wife *Halima* would not let him goe to *Constantinople,* unlesse he would carry her with him. But presently they did facilitate that, telling him, that in stead of the Christian which they were to buy, and must dye and be turn'd over-boord instead of *Leonisa, Halima* would serve excellently for that purpose, and none better, of whom he desired to be freed more then from death. With the same facilitie as he entertained this in his thought, with the like, did *Mahamut,* and *Ricardo,* yeeld thereunto.

And being firmely resolved thereon, that very day the *Cadi* breakes with *Halima* about the voyage which hee thought to make to *Constanti-nople,* to carrie the Christian to the *Grand-Signior*; by whose liberalitie, hee hoped hee should bee made the great *Cadi* of *Cayro,* or of *Con-stantinople. Halima* told him that shee liked very well of his determina-tion, thinking that hee would leave *Ricardo* at home. But when the *Cadi* had certified her that hee would carrie him along with him, and likewise *Mahamut*; shee beganne to change her opinion, and to dis-advise him from that, which before shee had advised him to doe. In fine, she concluded, that if he did not take her with him, she would in no hand give way to his going. The *Cadi* would not crosse her, but if she would needes have it so, her will should be his; thinking then with himselfe that he would quickly shake off that yoake, which lay so heavie on his necke.

All this while *Hazan Bashaw* was not carelesse in soliciting the *Cadi* to deliver up the Slave unto him, offering him mountaines of gold, having besides given him *Ricardo* before for nothing, whose ransome he prized at two thousand Crownes. All these gifts and promises wrought no further good with the *Cadi,* then to make him hasten the more his depar-ture: and so solicited by his desire, and by the importunities of *Hazan,* together with those of *Halima,* who likewise built vaine hopes in the Ayre. Within twenty dayes he had fitted and rigged up a *Bregantine* of fifteene bankes, manning it with voluntary Souldiers, lusty young able men, partly *Moores,* partly *Greeke* Christians. Therein he embarqued all his wealth, and *Halima* left not ought at home in her house of any moment, and entreated her husband that he would give her leave to carry with her, her Father and Mother, that they might see *Constantinople.* *Halima's* intention was the same with that of *Mahamut*; meaning to deale with him and *Ricardo,* that when they were on their voyage, they should make themselves Masters of the *Bregantine,* and goe away with it. But she would not open her minde, nor declare her selfe unto them, till she saw her self embarqued; and this too with a full purpose and resolution to goe to the Christians Countrey, and to returne to that Religion which she had first beene of, and to bee married to *Ricardo*; being verily perswaded, that carrying such store of wealth along with her, and turning Christian, he would not refuse to take her to wife.

In this interim, *Ricardo* had speech with *Leonisa,* and declared unto her his whole intention; and shee againe acquainted him with *Halima's* purpose, who had imparted the same unto her. They injoyned each other secresie, and recommending themselves to God, they stood expecting the day of their departure. Which being come, *Hazan* went forth, accompanying them with all his Souldiers to the Sea-side; and did not leave them, till they had hoysed sayle; neither did he take off his eye from the *Bregantine,* till hee had quite lost the sight of it. And it seemed that the Ayre, and breath of those sighes which the enamoured *Moore* vented forth, did fill and drive forward with greater force the sayles, which wafted away his soule.

But he, as one who a long time liv'd in such torment, oppressed by love that hee could take no rest, thinking on that which hee was to doe, that hee might not dye by the hands of his violent desires; omitted not to put that presently in execution, which with long deliberation and a resolute determination, hee had forecasted. And therefore in a Vessell of seventeene bankes which he had made readie in another Port, he clapt into her fifty Souldiers, all his friends and acquaintance, whom he had obliged unto him by many gifts and promises; giving them in charge, that they should put forth to Sea, set upon, and take the *Cadi's Bregantine,* and all the wealth that was in her, putting to the edge of the sword as many as went in her, save *Leonisa* the Captive, for she was the onely spoyle that he look't after, prizing her above all the other riches and treasure which were in the Vessell. He likewise gave order that they should sincke her, so that not any one thing might remaine, that might give any the least signe or token of their perdition.

The covetousnesse of the spoyle added wings to their feet, and courage to their hearts; howbeit they knew very well that they should find but little resistance in those of the *Bregantine,* in regard that they were disarmed, and without any the least suspition that any such un-expected accident should befall them. Two dayes had the *Bregantine* now gone in her intended course, which to the *Cadi* seemed two Ages; for the very first day of all, he would feigne have put in execution his determination: But his Slaves advised him, that the businesse must first be so carried that *Leonisa* should fall sicke, to give thereby some colour to her death, and that this would require some daies of sick-nesse. He did not like of that, but would have it given out that she died suddainly, and so quickely make an end of what they had pro-jected, by dispatching his Wife out of hand, that he might allay the heate of that fire, which by little and little went consuming his bowels. But in conclusion he must condiscend to that, which the other two thought fit.

Now in this meane while, *Halima* had declared her intent to *Mahamut,* and *Ricardo,* and they were readie to put it in execution, as soone as they had doubled the points of *Alexandria,* or passed by the Castles of *Natolia.* But the *Cadi* was so hasty with them, and so sharpe set, that they promised to performe the taske they undertooke, upon the first occasion that should offer it selfe unto them. And one day at the end of sixe, which they had sailed another Voyage, and that now it seemed to the *Cadi,* that the feigning of *Leonisa's* sicknesse was sufficient, he did importune his Slaves that they should conclude the next day with *Halima,* and throw her (wrapt up in a winding sheet) into the sea, saying; it was the Captive of the *Grand-Signior.*

The day afterwards beganne to breake, wherein (according to the intention of *Mahamut,* and *Ricardo*) was to be the accomplishment of their desires, or the end of their dayes; when loe, they might descry a Vessell, which with sayle and oare came chasing them. They were afraid that they were Christian Pirats, from whom neither the one nor the other could expect any good. For being such, the *Moores* feared to bee made Captives; and the Christians, that though they should get their libertie, they should lose their goods, and be stript of all they had. But *Mahamut* and *Ricardo* contented themselves with *Leonisa's,* and their owne libertie; yet notwithstanding this imagined hope, they much feared the insolencie of your Rovers at Sea, for they that follow such kinde of exercises, and make a common trade thereof, bee they of what Religion or Nation so ever, they usually are cruelly minded, and of an insolent condition.

They prepared to defend themselves, without forsaking their oares, and doing all that might bee done in such a case of necessity, and so suddaine. It was not long, a matter of two or three houres, little more or lesse, that they drew neerer and neerer, till they came within Canon-shot of them. Seing this, they strooke sayle, loosed their Oares, betooke themselves to their Armes, and expected their comming.

Howbeit, the *Cadi* bid them be of good cheere, and fear nothing, for the Vessell was *Turkish,* and would not doe them any harme. He commanded that a white flagge in token of peace should presently be set up, placing it on the yard-sayle of the Poope, because they might

the better discerne it, who being already blinded with covetousnesse and greedinesse of gaine, made up with great furie to boord the ill defended *Bregantine*.

Whilest this was in acting, *Mahamut* by chance turned his head aside, and perceived that from the West-ward there was a Galley comming up, and to his thinking of some twenty bankes, whereof he certified the *Cadi*; and some Christians which wrought at the Oare, sayd, that the Vessell they had descried, was of Christians. All which did but double their confusion and feare, holding them in suspence, not knowing what to doe; fearing and hoping such successe, as God should be pleased to give them.

By this time I conceive that the *Cadi* would have given (being in that straight that now hee was) to have found himselfe againe in *Nicosia*, all the hopes of his pleasure, so great was the confusion and amazement wherein he was, tho he were quickly put out of it by that first Vessell, which without respect to the Flagge of peace, or that which was due to their religion, did set upon that of the *Cadi* with such force and fury, that they wanted very little of sinking it. The *Cadi* presently knew those that had thus set upon them, for his eyes gave him assured notice that the Souldiers were of *Nicosia*. He soone guessed the cause of their comming, and by whom set a worke, and gave himselfe for a lost and dead man: and had it not beene that the Souldiers gave themselves more to the spoyle, then the slaughter, not a man of them had escaped alive.

But when they were most busie about their pillaging; a *Turke* cry'de out aloud unto them saying, Arme, arme (fellow Souldiers) for a Vessell of *Christians* is comming upon us. And he had good reason to say so, because the Vessell which *Cadi's Bregantine* descried, bare *Christian* flags, and very fiercely did set upon that of *Hazan*; but before they came to grapple with her, one from the Prowe demanded of them in the *Turkish* language what vessell that was, and whence?

They made answer, that it was *Hazans* the *Bashaw, Viceroy* of *Cyprus.*
Why then (replied the *Turke*) you being *Musoliman's* have set upon
and robbed this vessell wherein wee know goes the *Cadi* of *Nicosia?*
Whereunto they answered, that they knew no other cause, save that
they were commanded to take her; and that they as being his Souldiers,
in obedience unto him had done his command.

The Captaine of the second vessell who came in a Christian disguise; resting satisfied with that which he desired to know, fell off
from that of *Hazan,* and made towards that of the *Cadi;* and with the
very first volly of shot he gave them, he killed ten of those *Turkes* that
were in her; and presently after entered her with great courage and
speed. But they had scarce set their feet on the hatches, but *Cadi*
instantly knew that it was not a Christian that had thus set upon him;
but *Ali Bashaw* who was in love with *Leonisa,* who with the same
intent as *Hazan,* stood wayting his comming; and that hee might not
be knowne, had clad his Souldiers like Christians, to the end that by
this devise, his theft might not be discovered.

The *Cadi,* who knew the intentions of these Lovers, and traytours,
beganne in a loud voyce to vent his malice, saying; what is this thou
doest, (thou Traytour *Ali Bashaw*) that thou being a *Musoliman,* that is
to say, a *Turke,* settest upon mee as a Christian? And you Traytours,
Hazans Souldiers, what a Devill hath moved you to commit so great
an outrage? for that to fulfill the lascivious and lustfull appetite of him
who sent you hither, will thus go against your naturall Lord.

Vpon these words of his, all of them silenced their Armes, no more
clattering was heard; and looking one upon another, they came at
last to know each other, because they had all of them beene Souldiers of one and the same Captaine, and served under one and the
same banner. And being now abashed at the *Cadi's* word, and
ashamed of their owne bad act; the points of their *Cimiters* were
blunted, and the edges of them dulled, their courages were quelled,

and their mindes mightily dismayed. Onely *Ali* shut his eyes, and eares, to all that hee saw, or heard; and falling upon the *Cadi,* he gave him such a cut in the head, that if the blow had not beene borne off by a hundred yards of *Calico* wrapt about it, doubtlesse hee had cleft his head asunder, yet it ſtrooke him downe between the bankes of the Vessell; and being fallen, the *Cadi* sayd: O cruell *Renegado,* enemie of our Prophet, and is it possible, that there is none that will chaſtice thy crueltie, and this thy great insolencie? How, (accursed as thou art) durſt thou presume to lay hands and draw thy sword againſt thy *Cadi,* and a miniſter of *Mahomet*?

These words added force, to force, and more fuell to the former fire; the which being heard by *Hazans* Souldiers, and moved with feare that *Ali* his Souldiers would take their prey from them (which they held yet to bee theirs) they determined to put all upon adventure; and one beginning firſt, and all the reſt following after, they set upon the Souldiers of *Ali* with such haſte, rancour, and courage; that in a little while they behaved themselves so manfully, that though they were more by many then they, they reduced them to a very small num⁄ber; but they which remained of them, tooke heart unto them, leaving scarse foure of *Hazans* men alive, and those very sorely wounded.

Ricardo, and *Mahamut* ſtood looking on, who ever and anon put their heads out of the scupper⁄holes of the Poope Cabbin, to see what would become of this great fray, which on both sides was so hotly pursued. And seeing that the *Turkes* were in a manner all slaine, and they that were alive, sore wounded, and how easily they might make an end of all of them, he called to *Mahamut,* and two kinsmen of *Halima* whom she had wrought to embarque themselves with her, that they might assiſt in going away with the Vessell, and with their helpe, and her fathers, taking up the *Cimiters* of the slaine, they shewed them⁄selves upon the Decke, crying out, Liberty, Liberty; and being aided by the Voluntaries who were *Greek* Chriſtians, with a great deale of ease, and without receiving any one wound, they cut the throats of them all; and boording *Ali's* Galley, which they found without defence, they took it, with all that was therein. Of those that dyed in the second encounter, one of the first was *Ali Bashaw,* whom a *Turke* in revenge of the *Cadi* ran through the body.

Being now Masters of all the three Vessells, they consulted what was now best to be done; in the end they yeelded to *Ricardo's* advice, which was, that they should take out all things that were of any price or valew, both in their owne, and *Hazans* vessell, and stow them in *Ali's* Galley, which was a vessell of farre greater burthen, and fitter to take in the lading, and make good their voyage; and the rather, for that the Rowers were Christians, who resting wel contented with their recovered liberty, and with many other good things which *Ricardo* liberally shared amongst them, offered to carry him to *Trapana,* and if need were, even to the end of the World.

This being thus ordered, *Mahamut* and *Ricardo* full of joy for this their good successe, went to the *Moore Halima,* and told her, that if she would returne to *Cyprus,* they would man her owne vessell with good valiant Voluntaries, and give her the one halfe of the goods which she had embarqued. But she, who notwithstanding this so great a calamitie, had not yet lost that itching love, and amourous affection which shee bare to *Ricardo,* told him; that shee would goe with him to the Land of Christians, whereof her Parents were wondrous glad.

The *Cadi* was by this time come to himselfe, and having drest and bound up his wound, as their haste and the place would permit; they likewise told him that hee should make choice of one of these two, either to go with them to the Land of Christians, or to returne in the same Vessell he set forth to *Nicosia.* Whereunto he answered, that since his ill fortune had brought him to such bad tearmes, hee would rather accept of the libertie which they gave him, and that he would goe to *Constantinople,* and make his complaint to the *Grand-Signior,* of

the great and grievous wrong which from *Hazan,* and *Ali* he had received. But when he knew that *Halima* would leave him and turne Christian, he was almost ready to run mad.

In conclusion, they man'd his owne Vessell, and furnished him with all things necessarie for his voyage, and gave him some *Chequines,* of those which once had beene his owne. And so having taken his leave of all of them, being resolved to returne to *Nicosia,* he besought before he had hoysed sayle, that *Leonisa* would doe him the favour to embrace him; for that grace and honour shee therein should shew him, would of it selfe bee sufficient to make him forget all his misfortune. All of them entreated *Leonisa* to conferre that favour on one that lov'd her so well, since in so doing, shee should not goe against the *decorum* and decencie of her honestie. *Leonisa* yeelded to their request, and the *Cadi* further entreated of her, that shee would but lay her hands upon his head, for that he hoped that imposition would heale his wound. *Leonisa* to give him content, condiscended thereunto. This done, and having bored many holes in *Hazans* Vessell, a fresh East winde favouring them, which seemed to court the sayles, and wooe them, that they might be admitted to come into them, did set them going amaine; so that in a verie few houres they lost the sight of the *Cadi's Bregantine,* who with tears in his eyes, stood looking how the windes carried away his wealth, his Wife, and with *Leonisa,* his soules delight.

With different thoughts from the *Cadi's* sailed *Ricardo,* and *Mahamut.* And so not being willing to touch any where; as they went along on Land, they past by the Towne of *Alexandria,* lanching through the deepe Gulfe; and without striking sayle, or being driven to make use of their Oares, they came to the strong Island of *Corsu,* where they tooke in fresh water; and presently without any farther stay, they passed by those noted high Cliffes, the *Acrocerauros.* And the second day, they discovered afar off *Paquino,* the *Promontorie* of the most fertile

Tinacria: out of whose sight, and that famous Island of *Malta* they went flying, for with no lesse swiftnesse did this happie bottome beare them.

In fine, compassing that Island, some 4. daies after they descried *Lampadosia,* and anon after the Island where they had like to have been wrack't, and the Galley wherein *Leonisa* was split against the rocks, the very sight wherof made her to tremble, calling to mind the danger wherein she had so lately seene her selfe. The day following they might ken before them their desired and beloved Countrey, which quickned that ioy which was alreadie in their hearts; their spirits were transported with this new contentment, which is one of the greatest which can be had in this life, to arrive after a long captivity safe in their owne native Countrey. And the next that may be equalled with it, is that which men receive in getting the victory over their enemies.

They found in the Galley a great chest full of flags and streamers of silk of sundry colours, with which *Ricardo* caused the Galley to be adorned in most gallant manner. The day was but newly broken, when as they found themselves to be within lesse then a league of the Citie, and rowing lustily, and sending forth ever and anone, shoutings of ioy and gladnesse; they slacked their Oares the neerer they came to the Haven, making in very leisurely. In her entring into the Port, an infinite number of people in an instant appeared; who having seene how slowly that well trimmed Vessell made to Land, there was not any one in all the whole Citie, which did not come forth hastning to the Sea side.

Whilest they were thus flocking to the shoare, *Ricardo,* entreated *Leonisa* that shee would cloath and adorne her selfe in the same manner, as when she entered into the Tent of the *Bashaw's,* because hee would put a pretty jeast upon her Parents. She did so, and adding gallantrie to gallantrie, Pearles, to Pearles, and beautie, to beautie, (which the hearts contentment commonly encreaseth) she attired and drest her selfe in such sort, as caused a new admiration and wonder. *Ricardo* also put himselfe into the Turkish habit, the like did *Mahamut,* and all those Christians that ply'de the Oare, for there were rayments enough of the slaine *Turkes* to serve all of them. When they arrived at the Port, it was about eight of the clocke in the morning, which showed it selfe so fair, and so cleare, that it seemed to appeare so of purpose, for to behold that joyfull entrance.

Before their entering the Port, *Ricardo* made them to discharge their Peeces of Ordnance belonging to the Galley; to wit, one Canon, and two Falcons, the Citie answered them with the like. The people stood as thicke as they could stand together, expecting the comming in of this goodly Vessell, so bravely waving her flying flagges and streamers, moving too and fro with a gentle gale of winde. But when they were come so neere them as to discerne that they were *Turkish,* by reason of those white *Turbants* that they wore on their heads, they beganne to waxe fearefull, and jealous of some fraud and deceit. Whereupon they betooke them to their Armes, and as many as were train'd Souldiers in the Citie, hastned to the Port, whilest the Horse-men went some one way, some another, scouring the coast. Of all which stirre they tooke great pleasure, who by little and little drew neerer and neerer till they entred the Haven, and casting anchor neere the shoare, throwing out a plank, and pulling in their Oares one by one, as it were in procession came on Land, which with teares of joy they kissed againe and againe; an evident signe that they were Christians, who had made prize of that Vessell. The last that landed, were the Father and Mother of *Halima,* and her kinsmen, all (as wee told you) clad after the *Turkish* fashion. That which made up the totall summe or finall end of all, was faire *Leonisa,* having a vayle cast over her face of Crimson Taffata, led by *Ricardo,* and *Mahamut*; which spectacle drew after them the eyes of all that infinite multitude, who at their landing proſtrating themselves as the reſt did, saluting the earth with their kisses.

By that time this was done, the Captaine and Governour of the Citie was come up unto them, who knew very well that they of all the reſt were the chiefe and principall persons. But he had scarce come fully neere them, but presently he knew *Ricardo,* and ranne with open arms, and signes of exceeding great joy to embrace him.

There came along with the governour *Cornelio* and his Parents, and those of *Leonisa,* with all her kinsfolke, together with those of *Ricardo*; all which were the greateſt Persons of rancke and qualitie in the whole Citie. *Ricardo* embraced the Governour, and repayed them all with thanks, that gave him the *Parabien* of his returne.

He tooke *Cornelio* by the hand, who as soone as he knew him, and found that he held him faſt, his colour began to change, and beganne to shake and tremble for feare; and taking *Leonisa* likewise by the hand, he sayd: Gentlemen, of curtesie (sirs) I beseech you, that before wee enter the Citie, and into the Temple to give due thankes unto our Lord God, for the great favours which he hath done for us in our misfortunes, you will bee pleased to heare mee speake a few words, which I am desirous to deliver unto you.

Whereunto the Governour answered, that hee might utter what he would; for they should all with much content and silence, give him both a willing, and attentive eare. Presently hereupon all the chiefeſt amongſt them, placed themselves round about him; and hee raising his voyce to such a height as he might (not overſtraining it) be well heard, spake unto them after this manner.

Gentlemen, yee may well remember the misfortune which some moneths since befell me in the Garden neere the Salt⁄pits, together with the losse of *Leonisa*; it cannot likewise have fallen out of your memorie, the diligence which I used in procuring her libertie, since that being forgetfull of mine owne, I offered for her ransome all my

whole estate. And though this perhaps to your seeming, was then accounted great *Liberalitie,* yet can it not, neither ought it to redound to my praise, since that I was to give it for the ransome of my soule. That which from that time since hath happened to both of us, will require long time, a more seasonable conjuncture, and another tongue lesse troubled then mine. Let it suffice for the present that I tell you, that after many various and strange accidents, and after a thousand lost hopes of remedying our misfortunes, Heaven taking pitie of us without any merit of ours, hath returned us home to our native Countrey, as full of content, as abounding in wealth: yet neither from this, nor my procured libertie is the end answerable to my desire; nor doe I take any great contentment in the enjoying of these, but in that which I conceive, this both in peace, and war my sweet enemie taketh, as well for to see her selfe free, as to see here before her (as she doth) the image of her owne soule. Yet notwithstanding I greatly rejoyce in this generall rejoycing, which they receive who have beene my companions in miserie; and though hard misfortunes, and sad mischances are wont to alter our dispositions, and to depresse valiant mindes. Yet was it not so with the overthrower of my good hopes; for I may bee bold to say it, that she amidst these her miseries, hath with the more undaunted courage and constant resolution, endured the shipwracke of her disadventures, and the encounters of my earnest, but honest importunings. Wherein that old Adage is verified; they may change their Countries, but not their Customes who have once gotten a habite of them. Of all this which I have sayd, I thence inferre; that I offered my whole estate for her ransome, gave her my soule in my good desires, plotted the meanes of her libertie, and adventured more for her, then my self, my life. And though from all these, (in the construction of noble, and ingenious dispositions) may be raised ingagements of some moment, yet will I not presse any one upon her, save onely this one which I presume she will make good; and in saying this, he puts up his hand, and in a very civill and mannerly way, tooke away the scarfe from before *Leonisa's* face, which resembled as it were the removing of a cloud, which darkens the beautifull brightnesse of the Sunne. Then did he prosecute his speech, saying; Loe, here (*Cornelio*) I deliver unto thee such a jewell, which thou oughtest to esteeme above all those things that are esteemed worthie. And so here (thou faire *Leonisa*) I give thee that which thou hast ever had in thy memorie. This if you please you may tearme *Liberalitie*: In comparison whereof, to give away my estate, my life, my honour, is all as nothing. Take her (oh thou fortunate yong man) take her (I say;) and if thy knowledge can but come to reach so high as to come to know her worth, I shall hold thee to be the happiest man this day on earth. Together with her, I will give thee likewise as much as comes to my share of all that which Heaven hath allotted to us all, which I make account will come to above 30. thousand Crownes. All this mayest thou freely enjoy with much pleasure, quietude, and content; and Heaven grant that it may continue many long and happie yeares. As for my selfe, being made unfortunate by some squint-eyed starre at my birth, since that I must be without *Leonisa,* I am content to be poore; for he lives too long who lives without *Leonisa.*

This sayd, he was silent, as if he had knit a knot upon his tongue. But within a very little while, before that any other spake, recollecting himselfe, he said; Oh Heavens! how do pinching troubles disturbe the understanding? I (gentlemen) out of the desire which I have to doe good, have not weighed well what I sayd. For it is not possible that a man should shew himself liberall of that which is anothers, not his owne. What jurisdiction or power have I in *Leonisa,* for to give her unto another? or how can I make offer of that which is so farre from being mine? *Leonisa* is his, and so much his; that were her Parents dead, (but long may they live) her affection would finde no opposition. And if there may stand perhaps in her way those obligations, which (being as she is, discreet) she ought to thinke she owes me; from this day forward I disclaime them, cancell them, and acknowledge them to be wholy voyd and of none effect; and therefore unsay what I sayd before. I give then to *Cornelio* nothing, because I cannot; onely I confirme the grant of my goods made to *Leonisa,* without desiring or looking for any other recompence, save that shee esteeme for true my honest thoughts, and that she will have this beliefe of them, that they were never directed, nor looked towards any other point, save that which stood with her incomparable honestie, her great worth, and infinite beauty. And here *Ricardo* ended his speech.

Whereunto *Leonisa* answered in this manner; if any favours (oh *Ricardo*) you imagine I did *Cornelio* (when as you were enamoured and jealous of mee) imagine likewise, that it was both meete, and honest, as being guided by the will and order of my Parents, who intending to make a match betweene us; laid their command upon me to do him those favours. If you rest satisfied with this, well may you satisfie your selfe with that which experience hath made knowne unto you of my honestie, and reservednes. I speake this, for to give you (*Ricardo*) to understand, that my will was alwaies subject to anothers will; to wit, my Parents, whom I now most humbly (as is meet) beseech, and earnestly entreat, that they will give me leave and libertie, freely to dispose of that which your valour and *Liberalitie* hath bestowed on mee. Her Parents with a very good will gave her their leave so to do, relying on her discretion, that she would make use thereof in such sort, as should redound alwaies to her owne honour, and their profit.

Having obtained this licence, discreet *Leonisa* proceeded thus. I shall entreate you (as many as be here present) that you will beare me witnesse, that I had rather incurre the censure of lightnesse, and inconstancie, (which none of you all can, or shall ever be able to charge me therewith) then to bee taxed (which is hatefull both in the sight of God and man) of unthankfulnesse and ingratitude. And therefore (oh valiant *Ricardo*) my good will and affection hitherto so reserved, so perplexed and doubtfull, shall now declare it selfe in your favour. To the end, that you men may know that all women are not ingratefull, by my expressing of my thankfulnesse to you. I am thine (*Ricardo*) and will bee thine till death, if some better knowledge move thee not to deny me thy hand; for I desire nothing more then to have thee to be my Husband.

Ricardo hearing these words, was so transported with joy, and in a manner so besides himselfe, that hee neither knew how, nor could not answer *Leonisa* in any other language then humbling himselfe on his knees before her, and kissing her hands which hee held fast by force, bathing them often with his tender and loving teares. *Cornelio* did shed teares too, but of griefe, and sorrow; so did *Leonisa's* Parents, but of joy and gladnesse; and of admiration and contentment all the standers by.

The Bishop of that Citie was then there present, and with his Benediction, and Licence brought them to the Cathedrall Church, and dispensing with the time, instantly married them. The joyfull newes of this wedding was quickly spread over all *Trapana,* and that very night in token of rejoycing, infinite lights were set up, and great bonfires made, accompanied with ringing of bells, and divers loud musicall instruments. And for many daies after there were Maskings, Commedies, sporting with Canes, running of Bulls, and solemne invitations and feastings made by the Parents of *Ricardo,* and *Leonisa. Mahamut,* and *Halima* were reconciled to the Church, who impossibilited of fulfilling her desire in being *Ricardo's* wife, contented her selfe in matching with *Mahamut.* To *Halima's* Parents and kinsmen *Ricardo* gave liberally of those spoyles which he had taken, wherewith they might be enabled to live, not onely sufficiently, but plentifully. In conclusion, all of them remained fully contented and satisfied; and the fame of *Ricardo* going beyond the bounds of *Sicily,* spread it selfe through all the parts of *Italy,* and many other places under the name of the *Liberall Lover.* And even to this very day continueth fresh in those many Children which he had by *Leonisa,* who was a rare example of discretion, honestie, reservednesse, thankfulnesse, and beautie.